THE GENUS
ARUM

The Royal Botanic Gardens, Kew

A KEW MAGAZINE MONOGRAPH

The Genus
ARUM

Peter Boyce

Illustrations by
Pandora Sellars
Ann Farrer
and
Tim Galloway

Series Editor
Victoria Matthews

LONDON: HMSO

To my Mother

Printed in the United Kingdom for HMSO
Dd 293663 C15 4/93 531/3 12521

CONTENTS

LIST OF COLOUR PLATES

9

ACKNOWLEDGMENTS

I had originally planned to make this chapter a brief paragraph just to thank everyone who has helped me throughout the four years that this revision has taken. However, as the project drew to a close, I realized that such an approach was totally unacceptable as a way of thanking the many people who have contributed.

Of my colleagues at Kew, the greatest debt of gratitude is owed to Dr Simon Mayo on whose extensive knowledge of the Araceae I have drawn unceasingly. Despite our innumerable discussions on almost every aspect of *Arum* and the Araceae, Dr Mayo's love for this family is as strong as ever. My heartfelt thanks also go to Dr John Dransfield who had the unenviable task of proof-reading my text and whose comments on some of my more blatant errors I shall always treasure. Thanks also go to Dr R.K. Brummitt whose guidance led me through the nomenclatural nightmare that accompanies *Arum*, Victoria Matthews who read and edited the final version of the text, and Brian Mathew who, aside from proof-reading several parts of the book, has added enormously to my knowledge of bulbous plants through his publications and discussions. A thank you must go to all of those in the Kew Herbarium who have endured *Arum* talk for so long and yet can still show interest in the subject!

Outside Kew, people without whose help this revision might never have been completed include Professor Neriman Özhatay and Dr Kerim Alpinar of the Botany Faculty, University of Istanbul who have welcomed me warmly on my visits there, Mr Josef Bogner of the Munich Botanical Garden, Professor John McNeill and Dr Robert Mill of the Royal Botanic Garden, Edinburgh, Dr Charles Jarvis of the Natural History Museum, London, Dr P. Heipko and Dr Thomas Raus of the Berlin Botanical Garden, Dr Arlich Kress of the Herbarium at the Munich Botanical Institute, Professor Ph. Moreau of the Laboratoire de Phanérogamie of the National Museum of Natural History, Paris, Dr Harald Riedl of the Natural History Museum of Vienna, and the Keepers and Curators of these institutes.

With regard to growing *Arum* I would like to thank Brian Halliwell and Tony Hall of the Living Collections Department at Kew. Among private growers the following have all been involved in some capacity with the work: Mike Tucker who owns perhaps the finest collection of *Arum* in the UK at present and has sent numerous specimens for me to study as well as providing some plants for illustration, Norman Stevens, a bulb grower on whose shoulders rests the honour of reintroducing two species into cultivation for only the second time in their history and Mike Salmon who has kept the stream of unidentified species coming sufficiently fast to prevent complacency.

Those not directly approached for assistance, but who have been more than willing to offer advice include Sir Colville Barclay, Mrs Mary Briggs, Mr Vaughn Fleming, Ms Deni Bown, Dr John Akeroyd and Dr Chris Preston.

I would like to thank Tim Galloway for the line illustrations, and for his patience, and Yvette Harvey for the maps.

Lastly I wish to express my thanks to Pandora Sellars and Ann Farrer without whose paintings this book would be a poor shadow of itself. Their ability to reproduce on paper what nature has taken millennia to perfect is still a source of wonder. I need add no further comment, the paintings in this volume say it all.

INTRODUCTION

The genus *Arum* consists of 25 species of tuberous plants occurring from the Azores to western China and from Sweden to Morocco. *Arum* belongs to the family Araceae (or aroids), which contains such well-known plants as *Monstera deliciosa* (the SWISS CHEESE PLANT) and *Philodendron scandens* (the SWEET-HEART VINE). Vegetatively arums are in general rather similar in appearance, but in flower, while conforming to a general pattern, they display a wide range of shape and colour, making them a rewarding group for the grower.

Many 'bulb' and alpine enthusiasts grow a couple of species of *Arum*, usually the showy *A. creticum* and *A. dioscoridis*, both of which are reasonably hardy in the open in southern Britain. In addition, many people are familiar with the widespread *A. maculatum*, used in the past as a source of starch and drugs and which has a host of common names: JACK IN THE PULPIT, WAKE ROBIN and CUCKOO PINT, to name but three (see Grigson (1955) for further names). There are, however, many species which are practically unknown except to a few enthusiasts, and it is one of the aims of this book to bring these attractive and interesting species to the attention of a wider audience. Most, if not all, are easy to grow. Even the few, more difficult, species only require a rich, well-drained compost in just frost-free conditions. Most of the species are perfectly happy in the open in southern Britain.

For the biologist the genus is fascinating. The pollination biology has been the subject of numerous accounts, while our knowledge of the chemistry of the genus is still expanding. *Arum* belongs to the tribe *Areae*, traditionally considered to be one of the most highly evolved in the *Araceae* and the genus has a complex pollination system. Where the species occur they are often the dominant geophyte.

Accurate identification in the genus has always been a major difficulty. The problem stems from an overzealous approach to the infrageneric taxonomy in the past. Too many species have been described without their variation being understood and with a poor knowledge of the living plants, either in cultivation or in the field. The one exception to this paucity of specific information is Prime's magnificent book *Lords and Ladies* (1960) which deals with the two

British species *A. maculatum* and *A. italicum* subsp. *neglectum* and is the only major work on the genus. Aside from this, the genus has remained for the most part poorly understood.

More recently, however, most of the species have been introduced into cultivation and this, coupled with extensive research into pollen, cytology and chemistry, has allowed the development of a more complete understanding of the species' limits. The present work builds on this and I hope that it will now be easier to name the species.

HISTORY OF THE GENUS

Linnaeus used the generic name *Arum* in his *Species Plantarum* (1753), taking up a name that had been widely used in the past. The first record of its use as a generic name is that of Fuchs (1542). Lobelius (1576) used the name *Arum officinarum* to describe the spotted form of *A. maculatum*. The first record of the latter name is that by Tabernaemontanus (1590). Tournefort (1719) attempted to clarify the correct application of *A. maculatum* and as a result of his work, Linnaeus adopted the binomial that is used today. However, the name *Arum* and the history of the plant goes back much further. The first record of the name *Arum* is in classical Greek literature, both Pliny and Dioscoridis giving details of more than one species of *Arum* known to them. The word *Arum* comes from the Greek αρστ. Numerous theories have been put forward as to the meaning of the word (Prime, 1960).

Arum maculatum has more common names than almost any other plant. Indeed, according to some estimates there are more than one hundred. Almost all of the common English names are derived from the plants' appearance in flower. For example CUCKOO PINT is derived from the Anglo-Saxon *cucu pintle* (*cucu* = lively, *pintle* = penis) in allusion to the similarity of the sterile spadix-appendix to a penis. WAKE ROBIN also has sexual connotations, being derived from *cwic* (*cwic* being the same as *cucu*) and *robinet*, (French for cock). The name LORDS AND LADIES appears to be linked to the colour of the spadices, which vary between purple and yellow. It dates from Elizabethan times when noblemen ('lords') wore purple while their 'ladies' favoured paler colours such as yellow (Bown, 1988). A comprehensive list, together with a concise history of *A. maculatum* may be found in Grigson's *The Englishman's Flora* (1955).

The genus has been used as a source of starch, arrowroot, drugs and dubiously effective love potions for over a thousand years. Its greatest period of popularity came with the advent of ruffs in the Elizabethan period. The crushed tubers of *A. maculatum* and *A. italicum* subsp. *neglectum*, being rich in starch, were used to stiffen these fanciful additions to the costume of the day. In addition the use of the starch as a beard stiffener was recorded by at least one person during this period (Nashe, 1589). Its use was fairly short lived, however, because the tubers contain a caustic sap, as well as calcium oxalate crystals (raphides), which caused chapping and blistering of the hands. With the introduction of much safer forms of starch from rice and wheat, the use of *Arum* died out. In Scandinavia, where starch from the tubers of *A. alpinum* was used to stiffen clerical collars, there are numerous colonies of *A. alpinum* close to church sites (Nielson, pers. comm.).

The genus *Arum* was erected by Linnaeus (1753) to include not only *A. maculatum*, the type of the genus (see Green, 1929), but also numerous other species that have since been transferred to other genera within the Araceae. For example, *A. tenuifolium* later became the type of the genus *Biarum* Schott (1832). Since 1753 several hundred *Arum* names have been published. Many have been transferred to other genera, while many more have proved to be referable to previously named species. Despite the resulting plethora of names, new species are still being found today, even in well-known places.

Arum italicum was the next species to be validly named, by Phillip Miller (1768) in *Gardeners Dictionary*. This was followed by *A. pictum*, named by Linnaeus the younger (1782). With the beginning of an intensive period of botanical exploration from around 1810 onwards, the flood of new plants entering private collections brought with it several species of *Arum*. The first of these, *A. orientale*, was collected from an unknown locality in the Crimea or Caucasus and subsequently named by Marschall von Bieberstein. This species is widespread, occurring from southern Austria eastwards into southern Russia. The next species, *A. dioscoridis*, a plant well known to the ancient Greeks, was not introduced into northern Europe until some time in 1812 or 1813 when Sibthorp collected it on Cyprus. It was later named and illustrated by Smith in their joint undertaking on the flora of Greece (Smith in Sibthorp & Smith, 1813).

Between 1836 and 1851 three interesting and still uncommon taxa were described. *Arum jacquemontii*, published by Blume (1836), was discovered by the French collector Jacquemont and is remarkable for its distribution which extends into China and northern India; the original collection came from Central Asia. Also described by Blume (1836) was *A. byzantinum*, which was based on an illustration in a seventeenth-century manuscript by Clusius. It has greenish white spathes and is restricted to woodlands in the vicinity of Istanbul. *Arum alpinum*, a delicate species from the Transylvanian Alps, was introduced in 1851 and described by Schott & Kotschy in the same year.

In 1853 four further species were described. *Arum creticum*, well known for its unique yellow inflorescences and powerful scent, was introduced by Heldreich from two sites on Crete where he collected it in 1847. Three Middle Eastern species were first collected by Boissier; *A. hygrophilum*, from the mountains around Zabadani in Syria, near the present-day Lebanese border, *A. palaestinum* from the slopes of Mount Carmel near Jerusalem and finally *A. rupicola*, with its narrow green and purple spathes, was described by Boissier (1853) from material collected in present-day Lebanon. This name has generally been overlooked since and is the correct name of the species widely known as *A. conophalloides* or *A. detruncatum*.

In subsequent years several other taxa were introduced, a few of which are quite well known in gardens today. A delightfully sweet-smelling plant collected in the Lebanon was named as *A. gratum* by Schott (1856). Two more new species were published in 1857. *Arum nigrum*, described by Schott (1857b), is a showy, deep purple-spathed plant from the Dalmatian Alps and *A. elongatum*, named by Steven (1857), is a large, handsome species, again with purple spathes, from southern Russia, Asia Minor and the Balkans.

Schott's *Prodromus Systematis Aroidearum*, published in 1860, in-cluded descriptions of many new *Arum* species. Most of these are no longer recognized, and their names have become synonyms. *Arum concinnatum*, based on a collection made by Zelebor in western Turkey or the eastern Aegean, is still regarded as distinct. At the end of the nineteenth century *A. korolkowii* was described by Regel, based on a Korolkow collection from Turkestan. This species, regarded as du-bious by Engler (1920), is today rarely seen in cultivation.

Since the turn of the century several new species have been described. Hruby (1912) published a description of the Libyan species *A. cyrenaicum. Arum lucanum* described by Cavara & Grande in 1911 from Italy, was regarded by Prime (1978) as a subspecies of *A. orientale* but is recognized here as a good species. *Arum idaeum*, a delightful Cretan endemic, was described by Cousturier & Gandoger in 1917 from material collected by them in 1914. Riedl (1981) described a collection made by Haines in 1961 from Ba'quba in Iraq as *A. hainesii*. Mill's research for the Araceae account in the *Flora of Turkey* highlighted that two species collected previously had been overlooked. One of these, *A. balansanum*, had been collected by Balansa in western Turkey and called *A. phrygium*, but had never been validly described. The second species, *A. euxinum* had been previously known as *A. incomptum*, a name based upon mixed material. Most recently *A. purpureospathum* with bright purple spathes has been described from Crete (Boyce, 1987a), while this monograph contains the validation of *A. apulum* from southern Italy, previously known as a variety of *A. nigrum*, but recently shown to be a distinct species by Bedalov (1984).

MORPHOLOGY

THE TUBER

The structure of the tuber in *Arum* is of fundamental importance for accurate identification of species. In fact, even sterile material is identifiable to section, providing details of the tuber are available.

Two types of tuber are found: horizontal-rhizomatous and discoid (see Figure 1, p. 19). Apart from the differences in shape implied by these terms, the tubers also display a marked difference in their growth habit.

The horizontal tuber grows in the same manner as a bearded *Iris*; it possesses a lateral (morphologically terminal) growing point from which the main shoot develops, and where the new tuber forms later in the year on the ripening and death of the aerial part of the growth. Apart from this main area of growth, adventitious buds are found along the length of the tuber which develop into vegetative shoots and subsequently form tubers during the course of the growing season. In time these tubers become detached from the parent plant and

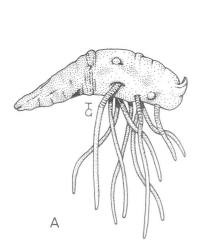

Figure 1. Tuber types: **A**, horizontal-rhizomatous (*A. concinnatum*); **B**, vertical-discoid (*A. alpinum*).

establish independent plants, so that extensive, spreading colonies are formed.

The other tuber type is discoid and not dissimilar to that of a tuberous-rooted *Begonia* in shape. The tuber bears a central growth-point from which the shoot develops. The tuber may be orientated with the growth-point uppermost (e.g. *A. idaeum*) or may lie on its side with the growth-point horizontal (e.g. *A. dioscoridis*). The new tuber forms on top of the old one, and contractile roots pull it further into the ground. Around the base of the main shoot are found dormant buds which give rise to new shoots and tubers. However, these buds often remain dormant unless the main shoot is damaged or destroyed. If tubers do develop from such buds they frequently remain attached to the plant. Thus species with discoid tubers form compact, congested colonies.

THE ROOTS

There are two types of root, contractile and feeding. At the beginning of the growth season, the plant produces a small number of relatively thick, unbranched roots from the shoot-base. These roots generally go down straight into the soil, anchoring the tuber which has spent the last four or five months rootless and thus insecure. Once the tuber is in a firm position, the much finer feeding roots start to develop. The feeding roots do not necessarily grow downwards, but instead form a dense mat, perhaps in response to the heavy but short-lived rains common in the areas where many species grow. The root mass is also doubtless very effective in taking up nutrients from the sparse soil in rock crevices and on stony hillsides, or when in competition with other actively growing plants. Towards the end of the growth season the feeding roots start to wither as the soil begins to dry out and at the same time the tough central core of tissue inside the spongy contractile roots begins to contract. By this time the root-tip is some half a metre below the soil surface and well secured, and so the new tuber is pulled down more deeply, bringing it to approximately the same depth as the parent tuber at the beginning of the growth period. This protects the tuber from undue heat and dryness during the dormant phase.

THE SHOOT AND LEAF

The growing point is enclosed by two or three cataphylls which serve to protect the developing shoot both underground and as it emerges. Ray (1987a) described cataphylls protecting seasonally resting buds as resting cataphylls.

In subgenus *Arum* the vegetative primordium starts growth either in autumn, winter or spring, depending on the species. If the emerging shoot is dissected it can be seen that each leaf emerges from the petiole-sheath of the previous one (see Figure 2, p. 21). Approximately two months into the growth cycle the inflorescence begins to develop. From quite early on, the reproductive organs are easily distinguishable in the developing inflorescence. With the emergence and maturation of the terminal leaf the inflorescence expands and emerges from the petiole-sheath of the terminal leaf.

The flowering pattern in subgenus *Gymnomesium* is somewhat

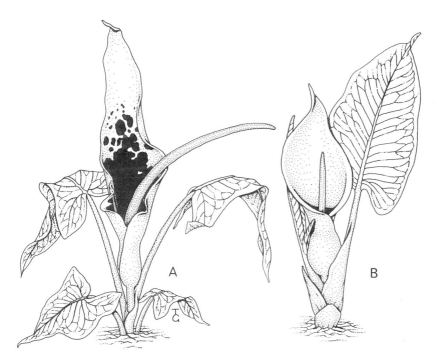

Figure 2. Comparison of flowering modes: **A**, spring-flowering, with the leaves beginning to wither prior to dying back for the summer rest (*A. dioscoridis*); **B**, autumn-flowering, coinciding with the appearance of new leaf growth (*A. pictum*).

different. In this subgenus, containing the one species *A. pictum*, the inflorescence emerges before the leaves, although occasionally the leaves are quite well developed before the spathe opens, especially if the plant has been forced in a glasshouse. The inflorescence is produced terminally from the previous year's shoot, the flowering being delayed until the autumn, when it coincides with the onset of the growth period. The inflorescence is subtended by two or three cataphylls and from between these the new season's growth emerges (see Figure 2, p. 21).

Arum displays a wide range of vegetative plasticity. A brief look at even a moderately large colony of a species reveals a wide range of leaf shape and size (see Figure 3, p. 23). With practice, however, it will be seen that a pattern is evident and it is possible to distinguish between certain species on the basis of leaf shape and coloration. At the extremes of leaf shape are the weakly lobed leaves of *A. euxinum* and the hastate leaves of *A. italicum*, but a wide range of intermediates can be found. It is worth noting when trying to identify *Arum* species that in many cases the first leaf to emerge is different, sometimes very much so, from leaves produced later in the season. The same can also be said of the final leaf. Furthermore, in *A. italicum* subsp. *neglectum*, there are two growth flushes, one in the autumn, the other in the spring, which give rise to leaves of quite different appearance. In fact it would be easy to assume that two species were involved.

The foliage displays a broad range of colour. The basic colour varies from pale green as in *A. hygrophilum* to deep green as in *A. orientale* and several species possess leaves with silver or grey blotches, black speckles, purple tinging or silvery grey veins. The petioles also show a wide colour range. Apart from plain green, in some species they are deep purple, in others pale green longitudinally striped with paler green, purple or greenish brown.

The study of stem organization in the Araceae has received considerably more attention than the leaf structure. However, very little of the work has any direct bearing on *Arum* and as such this is not the place to discuss the findings of the various researchers. For those who wish to delve more deeply into the subject I recommend that they look at the papers by Irmisch (1874), Engler (1877, 1879, 1905, 1911, 1915, 1920), Engler & Krause (1908, 1912, 1920), Krause (1908) and Ray (1987b).

THE INFLORESCENCE

In *Arum* the inflorescence is borne on a peduncle. The most conspicuous part of the inflorescence is the spathe. This is a bract of rather
complex shape, divided into a basal tube and an apical limb. The
spathe-tube is generally cylindric with free margins and has a constricted apex which partially limits access to pollinating insects.
However, in one species, *A. creticum*, the spathe-tube is open and
goblet-like. The colour of the spathe-tube is variable. Depending on
the species the interior may be greenish white, white or yellow, with or
without a horizontal purple band running around the middle. In a
few taxa the spathe-tube is purple in the upper half and white in the
lower half, and in three species (*A. euxinum*, *A. hygrophilum* and *A.
purpureospathum*) the spathe-tube is completely purple inside. The

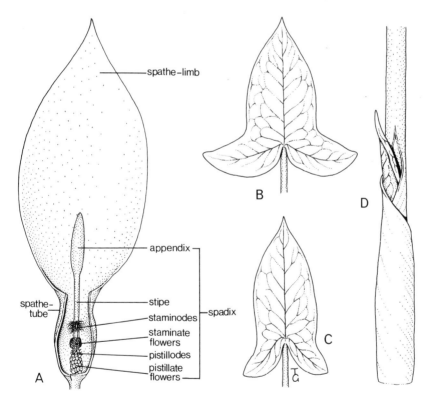

Figure 3. Inflorescence, leaves and petiole-sheath showing general morphology. **A,**
typical inflorescence. Variation in leaf shapes: **B,** hastate; **C,** sagittate. Petiole morphology: **D,** new leaf emerging from the petiole-sheath of the previous leaf.

23

outside of the spathe-tube is generally green, purple, white or yellow. In those species with green tubes, the green is sometimes overlaid by diffuse purple staining, especially along the margins.

The spathe-limb varies in shape from linear-lanceolate to broadly elliptic. The exterior colour ranges from almost pure white through various shades of green and purple to crimson. *Arum creticum* has a spathe-limb which is pale yellow both inside and out. The spathe-limb interior shows a similar wide range of colour. The base colour is, in some species, overlaid with varying degrees of staining and spotting, typically in shades of purple. However there are variations in the constancy of the spotting. In *A. dioscoridis* the spotting is a stable diagnostic feature. In *A. maculatum* and *A. italicum* the pale greenish white spathe is only occasionally marked with small, well-spaced, purplish black speckles. In the latter case the spotting is not consistent and of little use as a diagnostic character. Plants of *A. maculatum* and *A. italicum* with spotted spathes usually have similarly speckled leaves. The occurrence of spathe and leaf speckling in British populations of *A. maculatum* has been studied by Harmes (1982) who was unable to find any reliable taxonomic significance in its distribution. Apart from spotting, intensification of colour along the spathe margin is a common occurrence in a number of taxa, reaching its greatest development in *A. euxinum*. In this species the rather small pale greenish white spathe has a wide purple band along the margin, making it one of the most striking *Arum* species in Turkey.

THE SPADIX, STAMINODES, PISTILLODES AND FLOWERS

The spadix in *Arum* may be divided into two main parts: the appendix or sterile portion and the fertile portion. The very base of the spadix-appendix may be narrower than the rest, in which case it is described as stipitate; otherwise since it appears to be stalkless, it is described as sessile. The presence or absence of this stipe is an important diagnostic feature. The spadix-appendix ranges in shape from narrowly cylindric to stoutly conic-cylindric. The apex is either rounded or slightly pointed and at the base it may either taper gradually or be rather abruptly narrowed into the stipe. The adaptive significance of the presence of the stipe is not understood. Appendix colour may be cream, yellow, brown or various shades of purple and it may even vary within a single population. For example, yellow, purple and dull brown appendices can be found in one colony of *A. maculatum*. However, in any given species one colour generally predominates. The stipe is generally the same colour as the appendix.

The bristle-like staminodes and pistillodes present in *Arum* are of diagnostic importance. In most species two zones are found. The upper zone occurs above the staminate flowers, and may be interpreted as modified stamens. This view is supported by the occurrence of intermediate flowers with vestigial anthers on the interstice between the staminate flowers and the staminodes. The lower zone of bristles is situated above the pistillate flowers and is presumably derived from the pistillate flowers. The occurrence of intermediate pistillode structures seems to support this interpretation. Each staminode and pistillode consists of a basal portion which can be globose to compressed-globose, bulbiform, compressed-triangular or sometimes absent. The surface of this basal structure may be either smooth or somewhat roughened. My investigations into the occurrence of base sculpturing have revealed that possession of either rough or smooth bases is consistent in each species. In the rough-surfaced species, the epidermis, when magnified to $c. \times 20$, shows verrucate to papillate projections. The smooth-surfaced taxa at the same magnification display a waxy colliculate (bubbled) surface. The surface cells of the bristle are somewhat refractive and at higher magnifications ($c. \times 50$) vascular tissue is readily discernible through the thin walls of the bristle. The shape and colour of the bristle and its base differ from species to species.

The staminate flowers in *Arum* each consist of between two and four, fused, obovate anthers. The thecae are joined by a very short, slender connective and dehisce by a longitudinal slit (subgenus *Arum*) or a subapical pore (subgenus *Gymnomesium*). The colour of the anthers prior to dehiscence is diagnostic for many species and should be noted when observing plants in the field. The two most commonly encountered colours are yellow and purple, but cream, dull orange and purplish grey are found.

Arum pollen grains are free, not joined to form strands as in the genus *Dracunculus*. At anther dehiscence, most of the pollen falls to the bottom of the spathe-tube with very little remaining on the anthers. My observations of *A. dioscoridis* in southern Turkey, *A. maculatum* in England and *A. concinnatum* in Crete suggest that the pollen is picked up by insects crawling around inside the spathe-tube rather than by direct contact with the anthers. Similar observations have been made on *Dracunculus vulgaris* in Crete (Mayo, pers. comm.). Prime (1960) stated that *Arum* pollen is finely reticulate, but recently Grayum (1984), Bedalov (1985) and Bedalov & Hesse (1989) have shown that in all species studied, with the exception of *A. korolkowii*, the pollen has spinulose sculpturing. *Arum korolkowii* has scabrose sculpturing. Bedalov suggests that the degree of sculpturing may be useful in distinguishing between the various species. With the exception of *A. korolkowii* the differences are slight, however, and an extensive collection of photomicrographs would be necessary in order to make this a reliable method of identification.

Pistillate flower morphology and ovary colour is also useful for identification in *Arum*. The pistillate flower consists of a naked, sessile, oblong-ovoid gynoecium with a unilocular, multi-ovulate ovary. The ovules are orthotropous and attached to a single parietal placenta which lies on the outer side of the locule in relation to the spadix. The single placenta is thought to be a reduction from three (Engler, 1920), and a second placenta is not uncommon. The brush-like stigma is sessile, and generally off-white, greyish or purple. After the stigma has withered, a dull purple to brown pit remains at the ovary apex. The ovary ranges from green to cream and its apex is often a different colour to the ovary body – in some species the ovary is green with a bright purple apex.

THE FRUIT AND SEED

The morphology of the fruiting head in *Arum* is very uniform. The orange-red berries, borne in a clearly visible spike, suggest adaptation to bird dispersal. In some species of subgenus *Arum* (the 'cryptic' group, see p. 35), the peduncle undergoes a marked elongation during the maturation of the infructescence. In others (the 'flag' group) there is little or no elongation, although in both groups, thickening and hardening of the peduncle is observed. Subgenus *Gymnomesium* displays no such peduncle elongation.

The individual fruits contain between two and five seeds embedded in a clear, orange, viscous pulp which is almost certainly derived from the degeneration of the funicles, trichomes and placenta hairs (Prime, 1960; French, 1987b). The pulp also contains varying amounts of calcium oxalate crystals. From personal experience gained by cleaning seed, *A. pictum* contains the most while *A. hygrophilum* has little or none.

The seed structure of the various species is uniform with regard to gross morphology. Each seed consists of a leathery, reticulate testa, enclosing the copious, starchy endosperm. This reticulate testa deserves closer study. Even a cursory examination of the seeds of different species reveals subtle but distinct variations in the form of patterning. Riedl (1985) noted that taxonomically difficult species might be more readily separable using seed sculpture characteristics. Harmes (1986) carried out a systematic survey of seed size and number per berry in *A. maculatum*. He discovered that the size of the seed was directly linked to the number of seeds in the fruit. The fewer seeds present in the fruit, the higher the mean size of the seeds.

GERMINATION

Two types of germination strategy are found in *Arum*. Those species not subjected to cold winter temperatures, e.g. *A. dioscoridis*, *A. nigrum* and *A. pictum* germinate, produce an eophyll (the first seedling leaf with a defined blade) and a initiate a tuber more or less simultaneously. The eophyll appears above ground within a few days of germination. In species subjected to low winter temperatures, e.g. *A. alpinum*, *A. maculatum* and *A. idaeum*, germination occurs without any sign of growth above ground. Instead a rather large tuber is produced which remains below ground without producing any foliage for the first growing season. Not until the start of the second growing season does aerial growth appear.

The advantage of these strategies is not immediately apparent. It might be that plants subjected to low winter temperatures have to build up sufficient reserves below ground to survive the first dormant period after germination and that the plants from warmer habitats do not. However, since starch, the main constituent of the *Arum* tuber, is produced by photosynthesis, it would appear more logical for the plant requiring greater dormant-period reserves to produce foliage during the first growth season.

ANATOMY

While the anatomy of the Araceae has, on the whole, been quite thoroughly investigated, e.g. French (1985a, 1985b, 1986a, 1986b, 1986c, 1987a, 1987b, 1987c, 1988) and French & Tomlinson (1981a, 1981b, 1981c, 1981d, 1983), *Arum* itself has received little detailed attention.

French investigated both the anatomical structure of the anther-walls (1986a) and the type of vasculature which leads into the stamen (1986b). In the case of the endothecial (anther-wall) structure, he found that the patterning was similar for all the genera of the subtribe *Arinae*, which includes *Arum*. The endothecium consists of rectangular cells with anticlinal (perpendicular to the cell-wall) wall thickenings. French concluded that the shape of these thickenings varied considerably from species to species, citing the distinctiveness of the thickenings in *A. creticum* and *A. palaestinum* as examples. Although French stated that the overlap of endothecium structure throughout the family means that its use as a supraspecific systematic feature is limited, I suspect that the differences he found in *Arum* may prove to be of use in connexion with species delimitation.

With regard to stamen vasculature, French (1986b) reported that anastomosing vascular bundles are restricted to those genera of the tribe *Areae* possessing large stamens, of which *Arum* is a typical example. In *Arum* and the related *Eminium*, between two and five vascular bundles are found to enter each stamen. Some of these bundles are fused, leaving one to three unbranched bundles. Although French's research showed some variation within the *Areae*, it further confirmed that the tribe is a natural one.

The presence of trichomes in the ovary has been noted elsewhere in this book (see p. 26). French (1987b) expressed the view, shared by Dalmer (1880), that trichomes are associated with mucilage production, the mucilage acting as a 'bridge' through which the pollen-tubes reach the micropyle from the stylar canal. Engler (1920) reported that the disintegration of the trichomes was part of this mucilage production, although French found that mucilage was associated with whole trichomes, which suggests a different system. French stated that there is a good correlation between the presence of trichomes and the occurrence of mucilage. Although trichomes were present in virtually all members of the Araceae investigated, French failed to find the branched trichomes reported for *Arum* by Dalmer (1880).

CHEMISTRY

The high starch content of the tuber has long been known, the use of the tubers of *A. maculatum* and *A. italicum* subsp. *neglectum* for clothes starch dating back to the early sixteenth century. Heim, Chaulinguet & Hebert (1897) showed that a saponin, arin, is present in large quantities in the dormant tuber and in the aerial parts of growing plants. Chemical analysis of the tuber has been carried out more recently (Fernandez, 1952; Alpinar, 1985), the results of which suggest that the chemical composition of the tubers may be of significant taxonomic value.

The poisonous properties of the stems and leaves are well known. A series of experiments by Heim, Chaulinguet & Hebert (1897) suggested that *A. maculatum* and *A. italicum* contain tiny amounts of an alkaloid similar to coniine, the active poison in HEMLOCK (*Conium maculatum* L.). Recently, however, doubt has been cast on this result (Frohne & Pfander, 1984).

Arum also contains large quantities of calcium oxalate as a waste product in the form of needle-shaped crystals or rhapides that occur in the cells of all parts of the plant. The effect of these crystals and the chemicals they carry is felt as itching and burning of tender skin on picking and bruising the plants. In young children the effects can be serious enough to require medical treatment.

A short note by Lecat (1942) also reported the presence of ascorbic acid in three aroid genera, including *Arum maculatum* and *A. italicum*.

Most research into the chemistry of the inflorescence has been concerned with the physiological processes that occur inside the spadix-appendix during flowering (see p. 35). However, the composition of the odours has also been analyzed. In *Arum* and a number of related genera the foul odours are due to indole, skatole and some free ammonia (Smith & Meeuse, 1966; Chen & Meeuse, 1971; Meeuse & Raskin, 1988). The ammonia released from *A. dioscoridis* was clearly illustrated by its reaction with the vapour of concentrated hydrochloric acid (Meeuse & Raskin, 1988). To date, however, most odour analysis has been carried out not with *Arum*, but with *Sauromatum* which has the advantage of being easy to force into flower at any time. Further work on *Arum* is required before the composition of the floral odours can be used to any degree taxonomically.

CYTOLOGY

The cytology of the genus *Arum* has been studied by numerous workers and data are now available for almost all the species. As early as the 1920s chromosome counts were being published (Schmucker, 1925). More recently an exhaustive series of investigations by Marchant covering the whole of the Araceae appeared in *Kew Bulletin*. The papers which included *Arum* (Marchant, 1972, 1973) covered four species and since then about three-quarters of the species have been investigated.

The use of chromosome counts to determine the limits of poorly defined species has proved useful in the study of *Arum*. For example, the work of Gori (1958) on southern Italian populations of *A. nigrum*, which had been described by Carano as var. *apulum* in 1934, showed that they had a chromosome count of 2n = 56, as opposed to 2n = 28 in *A. nigrum*. Additionally it was later shown (Bedalov, 1973, 1980) that var. *apulum* is also distinct cytologically from *A. orientale* (2n = 28) which had been suggested as the true identity of the Italian plant. A similar study by Terpó (1973), produced evidence that *A. alpinum* is in fact distinct from *A. maculatum*, with which it had long been regarded as conspecific.

Bedalov (1981) has also shown that chromosome numbers are correlated to geographical distribution. The diploid species with discoid tubers all have fairly limited distributions, while the rhizomatous, polyploid species are, generally, far more widespread. The exception appears to be *A. alpinum* which is a diploid species and has a discoid tuber, but has, perhaps, the widest range in the genus. A similar study by Alpinar (1986) has confirmed Bedalov's findings.

Chromosome numbers have also been employed in the investigation of putative natural hybrids. In particular the work of Bedalov should be mentioned, concerning the hybrid *A. apulum* × *A. italicum* subsp. *italicum* that occurs in southern Italy (Bedalov, 1984), and that of Beuret (1971, 1972, 1977) and Kononov & Moljkova (1974), who showed that natural hybrids can be effectively investigated by chromosome studies.

Chromosome information is given in Table 1. In all cases the number given is that most commonly recorded, but it is worth noting that occasional differing counts have been made for some of the

33

species. In particular, *A. maculatum* has had the following published:
2n = 28, 56, 84 (Bedalov, 1981).

A more detailed list of diploid numbers recorded for *Arum* may
be found in the recent paper by Petersen (1989).

TABLE 1. Diploid chromosome numbers

A. alpinum	2n = 28	Terpó, 1973; Löve & Kjellqvist, 1973 – as *A. alpinum* subsp. *danicum*; Bedalov, 1981.
A. apulum	2n = 56	Gori, 1958.
A. byzantinum	2n = 28	Alpinar, 1986.
A. concinnatum	2n = 84	Alpinar, 1986 – as *A. nickelii*.
A. creticum	2n = 28	Marchant, 1972; Bedalov, 1981.
A. cyrenaicum	2n = 56	Marchant, 1973.
A. dioscoridis	2n = 28	Bedalov, 1981; Alpinar, 1986.
A. elongatum subsp. *elongatum*	2n = 28	Alpinar, 1986.
A. euxinum	2n = 28	Alpinar, 1986.
A. hygrophilum	2n = 28	Bedalov, 1978.
A. italicum subsp. *italicum*	2n = 84	Bedalov, 1981; Alpinar, 1986.
subsp. *albispathum*	2n = 56	Zakharyeva & Astanova, 1968; Zakharyeva & Makushenka, 1969.
subsp. *neglectum*	2n = 84	Lovis, 1954; Prime *et al.*, 1960.
A. korolkowii	2n = 28	Zakharyeva & Astanova, 1968; Zakharyeva & Makushenka, 1969.
A. lucanum	2n = 28	Marchi *et al.* 1974 – as *A. cylindraceum*.
A. maculatum	2n = 56	Lovis, 1954; Bedalov, 1982.
A. nigrum	2n = 28	Bedalov, 1973; Bedalov, 1975b.
A. orientale subsp. *orientale*	2n = 28	Zakharyeva & Astanova, 1968; Kononov & Moljkova, 1974.
subsp. *longispathum*	2n = 28	Bedalov, 1973; Bedalov, 1981.
A. palaestinum	2n = 28	Jones, 1957; Bedalov, 1978.
A. pictum	2n = 28	Contandriopoulos, 1962; Bedalov, 1978.
A. rupicola	2n = 28	Alpinar, 1976 – as *A. detruncatum*.

POLLINATION

Arum apparently attracts pollinators by deception. The spadix-appendix, which heats up soon after the inflorescence opens, is central to the mechanism of pollination. Heating up in the inflorescence, or thermogenesis, was noted in aroids by Lamarck as long ago as 1778 and has been the subject of numerous papers. Those by James & Beevers (1950) and, more recently, Meeuse (1975, 1985), Meeuse & Raskin (1988) and ap Rees *et al.* (1976, 1977) have shown that the process which causes thermogenesis is the rapid consumption of starch by a respiration system biochemically different to that normally found in plants, and known as cyanide insensitive respiration. This process produces much heat but little energy for the life processes of the plant. This apparently wasteful use of energy serves to vaporize odour compounds containing leucine, tyrosine, skatole and indole that are present on the spadix-appendix surface. These compounds produce the often foul odour which attracts pollinators.

In some of the *Arum* species the pollinators are insects that breed in dung, attracted to the dung- or urine-like smell of the inflorescence. Insects such as sand-flies and biting midges have recently been shown to be involved in the pollination of some Middle Eastern species.

Two main types of inflorescence are found in *Arum* (see Figure 4, p. 36). Those species with spathes held near ground level, below or just level with the leaves, ('cryptic' species) produce a scent of some kind, with the exception of *A. idaeum*. Those species bearing the inflorescence above leaf level ('flag' species) are scentless, apart from *A. creticum* (see p. 40).

Ecologically, the difference between the two types appears to be as follows: the 'cryptic' species, which include the British native *A. maculatum*, invariably grow in wooded or scrubby areas, whereas 'flag' species (*A. korolkowii*, *A. rupicola*, etc.) usually inhabit open or rocky areas with little or no overhead obstruction. Sometimes 'flag' species grow in clefts in rocky places. Therefore it seems reasonable to suppose that the two groups have distinct pollinators which behave differently. The 'cryptic' arums are presumably pollinated by insects attracted primarily by a scent stimulus, the 'flag' arums by those more responsive to a visual stimulus. Research by Arcangeli (1883), Knoll

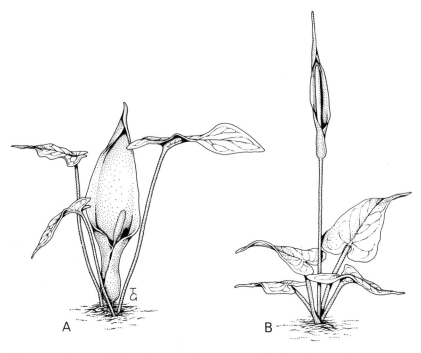

Figure 4. Flowering habits: **A**, cryptic (*A. maculatum*); **B**, flag (*A. rupicola*).

(1926), Kullenberg (1953), Prime (1960), Braverman & Koach (1982) and Koach (1986, 1987) has generally supported this.

Arcangeli (1883) found that, in southern Europe, a wide range of midges and gnats were attracted to *A. italicum* subsp. *italicum*, a 'cryptic' species, but that the greatest proportion were *Psychoda nervosa*, a dung-breeder and *Sciara nitidicollis*, a fungus-gnat. Knoll (1926), working with *A. nigrum*, another 'cryptic' species, found that mostly *Psychoda* spp. were attracted. Kullenberg (1953) reported a variety of *Coleoptera* and *Diptera* visiting *A. hygrophilum* and *A. dioscoridis* in the Lebanon. Prime (1960) reported that *A. maculatum* attracted female owl-midges, *Psychoda phalaenoides*, which lay their eggs only in dung and are possibly attracted to mates by scent. Prime speculated that *A. maculatum*, and perhaps *A. italicum*, produce a odour that mimics either the smell of the male *Psychoda*, or the breeding ground used by the female. Braverman & Koach (1982) found that the 'flag' species, *A. rupicola* (reported as *A. elongatum* and *A. conophalloides*), attracted three species of blood-feeding midges, *Culicoides* spp., all normally being parasites of birds. Koach (1986) also found that *A.*

hygrophilum, another 'flag' species, attracted blood-feeding sandflies, *Phlebotomous* spp. The occurrence of blood-feeding insects as possible pollinators of apparently scentless *Arum* species raises the question as to whether these species produce a scent undetectable to man. Braverman & Koach (1982) suggested that the warm spadix-appendix of *A. rupicola* might be coupled with a bird-like smell, at least in the Israeli population of this widespread species.

The most detailed research by Koach (1987) centred on the Israeli populations of *A. dioscoridis* and *A. palaestinum* – both 'cryptic' species. The strongly dung-scented *A. dioscoridis* was shown to attract staphylinid beetles, known dung-breeders, as well as various species of flies. This is mirrored in south-western Turkey, where *A. dioscoridis* attracts staphylinid beetles of the genera *Anotylus*, *Oxytelus* and *Atheta* (Drummond, pers. comm.). Koach reported that *A. palaestinum*, which typically smells of fermenting fruit, attracted fruit-flies (*Drosophila* spp.). In addition Koach's extensive research revealed a second ecotype of *A. palaestinum* which has a smell similar to that of *A. dioscoridis*, though weaker, and attracts beetles and flies. Further work is required to ascertain whether these ecotypes are morphologically and cytologically distinct.

More recently Drummond has began a series of pollination studies with the primary intention of identifying the insect species attracted to *Arum* inflorescences (Drummond & Hammond, 1991).

It is perhaps unfortunate that until recently researchers have tended to assume that the pattern of pollination biology known to occur in a few previously well-studied species applies to the whole genus. The more recent studies outlined above have shown that this is not the case. Most recently an historical overview of pollination in *A. maculatum*, including discussion of the over simplification that texts tend to favour, has been published by Lack & Diaz (1991).

The two species that form the basis of our detailed understanding of *Arum* pollination biology, *A. maculatum* and *A. nigrum*, are pollinated by dung-breeders; however, their pollination mechanisms are not identical.

There are several accounts of pollination in *A. maculatum*, the most comprehensive being that of Prime (1960), from which the following is largely compiled. The spathe opens in the late morning or during the afternoon, and although weather conditions and soil warmth appear to play a part in determining the time of opening, a series of experiments by Schmucker (1925) demonstrated that light is the major factor involved. The unfurling of the spathe reveals the spadix-appendix, which in *A. maculatum* is usually deep purple, although sometimes yellow or dull brown. Prime noted that the purple spadix-appendix formed a good contrast with the pale greenish white of the spathe-limb, and suggested that it may be visually attractive to *Diptera*. While this may be the case at short distances, the major attractant is smell, a fact demonstrated in a series of experiments by Lamb (1956).

On opening, the spadix-appendix of *A. maculatum* not only produces a foetid smell but also heats up quite markedly. It is generally agreed that the function of thermogenesis is to disperse the attractant odour (Smith & Meeuse, 1966).

Observations of flowering specimens reveal that the period of greatest odour production coincides with the receptivity of the stigmas. Meeuse & Raskin (1988) state that the 'trigger' for heat and thus odour production is a substance occurring in the staminate primordia. Originally called calorigen, this substance has recently been shown to be salicylic acid (Raskin *et al.*, 1987). By the time the stigmas have withered and the anthers dehisced, the spadix-appendix is scentless. Insects are thus attracted to the inflorescence as soon as the stigmas are receptive.

Both *A. maculatum* and *A. nigrum* attract species of *Psychoda* but pollinators' behaviour in approaching and entering the inflorescence is different. In *A. maculatum*, the midges fly towards the spadix-appendix and, spiralling towards the base, alight and crawl down over the staminodes into the spathe-tube. The insects make little attempt to escape, perhaps because the slippery surface of the wall of the spathe-tube prevents them from climbing upwards. However, crawling back up the spadix would not seem too difficult, since the staminodes do not fully block the spathe-tube entrance. The latter escape route is effectively prevented in *A. nigrum* by the slippery surface of the spadix (see below) and, as Prime (1960) noted, this may also be the case in *A. maculatum*.

The optical effects found in *A. maculatum* have not been fully researched. As Prime suggested, the visual effect of the purple staminodes, pistillodes, undehised anthers and banding around the middle of the spathe-tube may deceive the midges, once inside, that the mouth of the tube is in fact the base, hence trapping them by an optical illusion comparable to that in *A. nigrum* (see below).

Conditions inside the spathe-tube are good for keeping the

trapped insects alive, the humidity and warmth being supplemented by food when the stigmas wither and exude a drop of sugary fluid which the insects eat. Shortly after the stigmas wither the anthers dehisce, the staminodes and pistillodes shrink and the trapped insects escape. The stimulus to the insects to leave at this point may be that, with the withering of the staminodes and pistillodes, and the partial collapse of the spathe-limb, more light is allowed into the spathe-tube, thus guiding the insects out. Alternatively, as occurs in *A. nigrum*, the walls of the spathe-tube may become less slippery.

The pollination of *A. nigrum* differs in a number of ways from that of *A. maculatum*. The essential details of Knoll's exhaustive study (1926) are available in English, in a paper by Dormer (1960). Working in Dalmatia, Knoll discovered that while the exterior of the spathe-limb has both cuticle and numerous stomata, the interior is almost bereft of either. Instead, the surface of the spathe interior, as far down as the middle of the spathe-tube, is papillose, with every epidermal cell furnished with a downward pointing papilla. This papillose epidermis is oily.

Soon after sunrise the spathe unfurls and insects begin to gather in the vicinity, attracted by the strong dung-like smell of the spadix-appendix. The prospective pollinators land on the outside of the spathe-limb, and walk onto the inner surface. Here they are unable to maintain a grip on the oily surface, their struggles simply releasing more oil from the epidermal cells, and eventually they fall into the spathe-tube. Once trapped, escape by climbing out is prevented by the oily spathe-wall, and by the oily surface of the spadix above the pistillate flowers.

There appear to be two other features of the pollination mechanism of *A. nigrum* that further prevent trapped insects from attempting to leave too soon. The spathe-tube of *A. nigrum* is markedly bi-coloured, purple above and greenish white below. The coloration, combined with the hooded, deep purple spathe-limb, has the effect of making the strongest light source appear to be at the bottom of the spathe-tube. Since the insects trapped are attracted to light they stay at the base of the spathe-tube. The other feature concerns the fact that many insects will not attempt to fly unless they perceive a certain volume of open space around them. It seems that the form of the spathe-tube, in the fresh state at least, is such that the necessary volume is not apparent.

As with *A. maculatum*, conditions inside the spathe-tube of *A.*

nigrum are favourable for the insects and the stigmas secrete food. Similarly, scent production appears to be synchronized with the receptiveness of the stigmas. By the time the stigmas have withered and the anthers dehisced the smell is almost undetectable. At this time, although the spathe-limb and spathe-tube still offer no foothold, the spadix may be climbed and the trapped insects make their exit by this route.

In addition to noting these significant differences between *A. maculatum* and *A. nigrum*, Knoll's studies also suggested that the staminodes, and perhaps the pistillodes as well, have more than one function. Knoll found that many different dung-breeding and carrion-breeding insects were attracted to the foetid inflorescence of *A. nigrum*. Many of the small insect species fell into the spathe-tube as described above. However, some that alighted on the spathe-limb were far too large to effect pollination and, furthermore, if they did fall into the spathe-tube would make it difficult for other, smaller, insects to carry out pollination effectively. These large insects were prevented from falling in by the stiff staminodes at the entrance to the spathe-tube. Therefore, it appears that the staminodes, far from preventing the escape of desirable insects may, in some species at least, be present to prevent the entry of undesirable ones.

At the beginning of this chapter two exceptions to the 'cryptic' and 'flag' groups were mentioned. These species, *A. creticum* and *A. idaeum*, are closely related. Biologically both are poorly understood. At first sight *A. creticum* appears to belong to the 'flag' group but the strong lemon-and-freesia scent clearly excludes it. Similarly, *A. idaeum* should fit the 'cryptic' group except that the white inflorescences are scentless. It is probable that the pollination biology of both species is different from the rest of *Arum*.

ECOLOGY

Arum species show a preference for heavy, nutrient-rich, basic soils. Despite the wide range of distribution the genus is confined to five distinct types of habitat.

The commonest vegetation type encountered is that of garrigue, composed of low (often less than 50 cm), spiny and often aromatic shrubs on soils derived from limestone and typical of the Mediterranean. This habitat is seasonally dry, the greatest amount of rain falling in the autumn and winter; further north the winter rain may fall as snow. The plants' tuberous habit is ideally suited to this type of environment, especially since they are usually found with the tuber buried beneath boulders, or amongst low shrub, giving further protection. Plants of this habitat generally start growth in the autumn or early winter and either flower immediately, or grow through until the spring when they flower and set seed. With the cessation of wet weather in early summer they begin a dormant period until the following autumn. *Arum pictum* and *A. dioscoridis* are typical of this growth regime.

More rarely *Arum* species are encountered in maquis, which is a taller (2 m or more) vegetation type than garigue. *Arum dioscoridis* var. *syriacum* is an example of this, occurring amongst *Cotinus* and *Arbutus* along the coast of the Amanus region of Turkey.

A few species of *Arum* occur in deciduous woodland. In this habitat low summer light intensity rather than water stress is the major limiting factor on growth. The tubers enable the plants to remain dormant throughout the summer until autumn leaf-fall allows more light to reach the ground. *Arum maculatum* and *A. elongatum* are typical of this group. Variations on the deciduous woodland habitat are occasionally encountered, e.g. *A. elongatum* and the related *A. orientale* are found along the margins of coniferous forest in the Crimea and *A. italicum* subsp. *canariense* is found in evergreen *Laurus* forest on Tenerife.

The fourth habitat in which *Arum* grows is stream- and lake-side marsh. Only two species of *Arum* are regularly found in this type of habitat: *A. hygrophilum* in the Middle East and *A. euxinum* in northern Turkey.

A fifth habitat is that of rocky hillsides almost devoid of woody plants. Several species occur in this type of situation, although none appears to be restricted to it. There are no truly alpine *Arum* species. *Arum alpinum* is a deciduous woodland, or more rarely, garigue species, often occurring at low altitudes. It is only rarely found on grassy slopes in mountains. *Arum jacquemontii* occurs at the highest altitudes, to over 3,000 m in the Himalaya. *Arum idaeum* could be regarded as the most alpine species, as it usually occurs close to the snow-line in boulder rubble, often in association with true alpines such as *Anchusa caespitosa* Lam. and *Crocus oreocreticus* B.L. Burtt.

CULTIVATION

The cultivation of *Arum* usually presents few of the problems often associated with other 'bulbous' subjects, such as the provision of perfect drainage, and rigorously implemented rest and growth phases. This is not to say that the plants thrive on neglect but rather that they are far more tolerant of the occasional lapses in care than most 'bulbous' plants. Arums may be cultivated out-of-doors or under glass. If a comprehensive collection is maintained it will be found that both methods need to be employed in order to grow all the plants to their best. Those species that come from northerly countries require outdoor culture to succeed well. The more southerly species, which includes many of the most attractive ones, need protection from frost.

OUTDOOR CULTIVATION

The two major requirements for outdoor culture are the provision of a fertile, humus-rich soil, and a sunny, but not too hot, position. Soil preparation prior to planting should consist of the removal of all perennial weeds from the site and the incorporation of plenty of bulky compost if the soil is deficient in humus. Removal of perennial weeds is particularly important since, once established, *Arum* colonies are best left undisturbed.

A note on the purchase of tubers is worth making. Most bulb merchants sell tubers dry, dormant and unpotted. This is acceptable, but, if possible, the tubers should be checked before purchase. They should be plump, with no signs of shrivelling; there should be one or two shoots visible at the top or end of the tuber, depending on its shape (see p. 19). It is best to avoid those tubers which have numerous shoots since this usually indicates that the main growth-point has been damaged. Such plants will take considerably longer to settle down and flower. Damage, if recent or severe, may also lead to rotting later on. If a rhizomatous species is purchased, the cut end of the tuber should be checked to see that it has healed over or, if the cut is fresh, that it has been treated with a fungicide. If tubers are received by post a check should be made for any soft patches. These should be removed with a sharp knife, cutting back to sound tissue, and the cut surface then treated with fungicide.

Tubers are best planted immediately. If this is not possible they should be temporarily packed in damp peat with the growth-point uppermost and stored somewhere cool and light to prevent excessive etiolation of the shoots. A rather wide, flat-bottomed hole should be dug when planting. In general the tubers need to be approximately 9–10 cm deep and about 15–18 cm apart. If the soil is heavy, a generous layer of grit should be placed in the bottom of the hole. The tubers should be planted so that the growth point, when sufficiently developed to observe its orientation, is vertical. If shoots are not present at the time of planting discoid tubers should be set flat in the same manner as for *Crocus*. Species with rhizomatous tubers should be buried with the tuber lying horizontally. Once planted it is a good policy to mark the site to prevent the emerging shoots being damaged when hoeing. If some of the more tender species are to be tried out-of-doors, a well-drained, sunny position that does not receive early morning sun should be selected. The reason for this is that if the fleshy shoots freeze during the night they are far less prone to damage if they are allowed to thaw gradually; bright sun thawing frosted tissue can quickly lead to ruptured cells and the collapse of the plant.

Once planted, hardy arums require little attention for many years. It may eventually become necessary to lift and divide the clumps if they become too congested. A sure sign that the colony is in need of more room is the reduction of the leaf size and a marked decline in flowering. When division becomes necessary it should be done as soon as the plants have died down in early summer. The colony should be lifted with a fork and the largest tubers selected for replanting.

CULTIVATION UNDER GLASS

Most bulb growers cultivate arums in a cold- or bulb-frame. The bulb-frame (a glass-covered raised bed into which the bulbs are planted directly) offers a fair degree of flexibility. The compost used should be a fertile, gritty loam with about 25 per cent of its bulk comprised of humus. Once planted, a good watering to settle in the tubers is all that is required. When growth has started it is important not to allow the plants to dry out as this can severely check growth. The plants will also require feeding if they are to perform well. Two methods can be used: either a liquid feed applied with every other watering, or granular feed scattered on the soil surface at the start of the growth season. The latter method is convenient if the plants are to be left for long periods. Liquid feeding, however, allows much greater flexibility in the type of feed being given. A high nitrogen feed during the first three months of the growth period encourages good leaf development, while a high phosphate feed from just before flowering until dormancy encourages the development of a large, well-ripened tuber.

After flowering the leaves will deteriorate quickly, turning yellow and withering. At this time watering should be greatly reduced but not stopped. The temptation to remove the leaves should be resisted; it is best to wait until they are completely dead and brown when they will come away freely from the tuber. If the leaves are removed too early or pulled hard the new tuber is easily damaged, or even the growing point removed.

When the tubers are dormant the frame should not be allowed to become either too hot or too dry. It is best to allow the glass to remain open at the sides to allow air movement. In late August the frame should be given a thorough soaking and the side glass then replaced. This will break dormancy and ensure the development of a good root-system prior to the onset of cold weather.

Winter culture should consist of checking the plants occasionally for signs of slug damage and the potentially damaging grey mould. If heavy frosts are forecast the frame should be covered with several layers of carpet felt two or three hours before nightfall. This covering should be removed as soon as possible after sunrise the next day.

If the cold-frame or glasshouse is used for arum cultivation the choice of container is important. As stated above, most arums are tolerant plants. However for best results the provision of a fertile, moisture-retentive, but well-drained soil is important. Using clay pots is the easiest way to ensure that the plants receive sufficient water but do not suffer rotting caused by excessively wet roots. Unfortunately, clay pots of the size necessary to contain the larger species are both heavy and expensive. Many growers will wish to use plastic pots and, if the requirements of the species are understood these undoubtedly give good results. However, clay pots provide a greater margin for error.

Compost is really a matter of personal choice. For those already growing bulbs the richest mixture used (i.e. the compost for the larger 'Juno' *Iris* species) should be chosen. A suitable compost is: 2 parts moss peat, 1 part loam, 1 part 3 mm grit (not sand), dolomitic limestone to bring the pH to approximately 7.5 and base fertilizer at the recommended rate for John Innes No. 3.

Tubers should be potted in mid-summer, preferably before root growth starts. Arums soon exhaust the soil in even moderately large pots. For this reason annual repotting is necessary if vigour is to be maintained. On emptying the pot the tubers should be shaken free of compost, the dead roots removed and the tuber inspected for rot and pests. Any rot should be promptly dealt with as described on p. 50; for pests see p. 49. If the previous year's culture was successful the tubers should have increased in both size and number. It is important not to overcrowd the tubers, so provision of extra pots for excess tubers should be made in advance. Three flowering size tubers require a 15 cm pot. Pots are more suitable than pans as arums are rather deep-rooted and the deeper pots also retain more moisture. A piece of plastic gauze should be placed over the hole and the compost added to about half the depth of the pot. Usually the tubers need to be about 5 cm deep. They can be covered with more compost to within 2 cm of the top of the pot. The remainder of the pot should be filled with grit to suppress moss and liverwort growth, keep the 'neck' of the plant dry and give an attractive finish. Each pot must be labelled carefully to avoid mixing tubers. Once potted the tubers can be returned to their permanent growing position and given a thorough watering. The pots will need to be checked about twice a week until growth appears, to ensure that they have not dried out. Once growth has started the cultural directions above should be followed.

The major difference between pot and frame culture is the treatment of the potted plants during the resting phase. As with frame-grown plants watering should be reduced at the onset of yellowing of the foliage in summer. Once fully dormant the plants should be left in a warm and dry place. The pots must not be placed in full sun as this causes excessive drying out of the tubers. Despite the seasonally arid habitat of many species the tuber cannot withstand prolonged periods of heat and drought. It is worth noting that species naturally occurring in such environments invariably grow between rocks and beneath bushes that provide shelter and allow the retention of at least a small amount of soil moisture. The pots are best plunged to half their depth in sand which is kept barely damp. This will ensure that the tubers remain plump and reasonably cool.

In larger glasshouses a third method of cultivation is possible – the use of a free root-run bed. Two methods of construction can be used. The bed can be built by digging the glasshouse border to a depth of 45 cm and conditioning the soil with grit and peat if necessary. The tubers can then be planted as recommended for outdoor culture. If the glasshouse is set on concrete or a similar unsuitable base, the bed can be built using stout timber treated with a non-toxic preservative, or bricks. This should then be filled to a depth of about 4 cm with shingle and then a compost similar to that for pot culture. It will be found that all species will grow far more vigorously when treated in this way. It is especially beneficial for the creeping habit of the rhizomatous-tubered species which swiftly outgrow conventional containers.

PROPAGATION

The two main methods of propagation are by division and from seed. For many growers division will be preferred, since only two or three plants of each species are required. For those who wish to exchange with other growers, a couple of 'spares' of each species will be useful. However, if an extensive collection is desired, perhaps to demonstrate the variability of a species, then seed is preferable.

Dividing arums is straightforward. The ideal time for division is when the plants are dormant. However, plants grown in the open are then difficult to locate accurately. The problem can be resolved by, during the growing season, marking the position of the growing point with a cane. Once dug up the tuber can be checked for any rot and then replanted in its new position, or given to its new owner. Pot-grown plants are much easier to deal with. The best time to divide potted stock is when repotting. If a plant is required at any other time, the parent plant should be returned to its pot as soon as possible. Arums can be divided when growing if absolutely necessary. The division must be kept damp until it is replanted, and the parent plant should be well watered afterwards. Plants divided when in growth will often fail to flower. If they do produce an inflorescence it is good practice to cut it off as soon as the spathe is free of the petiole-sheath to help the plant to establish quickly.

Growing arums from seed requires patience but can be satisfying. On average it takes between four and five years from sowing to flowering, although *A. dioscoridis* and *A. pictum* may flower after three years. The treatment of the seed, whether fresh or packeted, is the same. If the orange-red pericarp is present it should be removed. If it is dried onto the seed, as is often the case with bought seed, the pericarp can be softened and then removed by soaking the seed in tepid water for about an hour. The pericarp should be removed for two reasons. First, it appears to contain a germination inhibitor; seed which is still surrounded by the pericarp is much slower in germinating. Secondly, the warm damp conditions required for germination are also ideal for the decomposition of the tissue of the pericarp. Germinating seed may rot when the flesh is not removed, probably because of infection by fungus from the decomposing pericarp. It is worth noting that the pericarp is both caustic and rich in rhaphides, and can cause quite severe burning to the hands. The wearing of rubber gloves or disposable surgical gloves is therefore recommended when cleaning the seed.

Once cleaned, the seed should be sown as soon as possible. Plastic pots are preferable. These do not dry out too quickly, and are also more easily cleaned than clay pots. Trays are not satisfactory because, on germinating, the seedlings begin to form a tuber immediately and the shallow nature of seed-trays can inhibit this severely. The pots should be filled with compost to within 2 cm of the top as recommended for mature plants. The seed can then be sown on the surface and just covered with more compost. The pots can then be topped up with grit and given a good soaking. The seed will germinate at the same time as the mature plants begin growth. If the seed is fresh it should germinate at the start of the next growth season, but if old or dry it may take up to a year longer. Seedlings of those species subjected to winter cold will spend their first growing season as under-ground tubers, showing no signs of aerial growth. They will not produce leaves until the start of the second growing season. It is most important that pots are not discarded for at least two years. As soon as the first leaf appears the pots should be given as much light as possible and not be allowed to dry out. At this stage the application of a half strength liquid feed at every watering ensures maximum growth in the first season. The plants should be kept under glass for the first year to allow the young tubers to attain a reasonable size.

The plants should be kept growing as long as possible during the

Plate 1

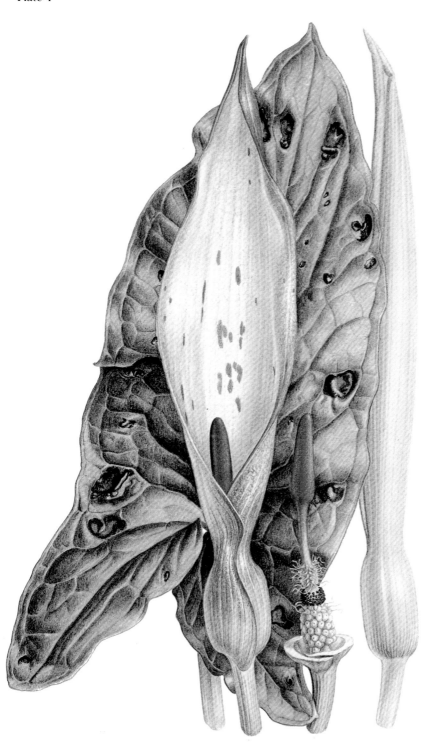

Arum maculatum

PANDORA SELLARS

Plate 2

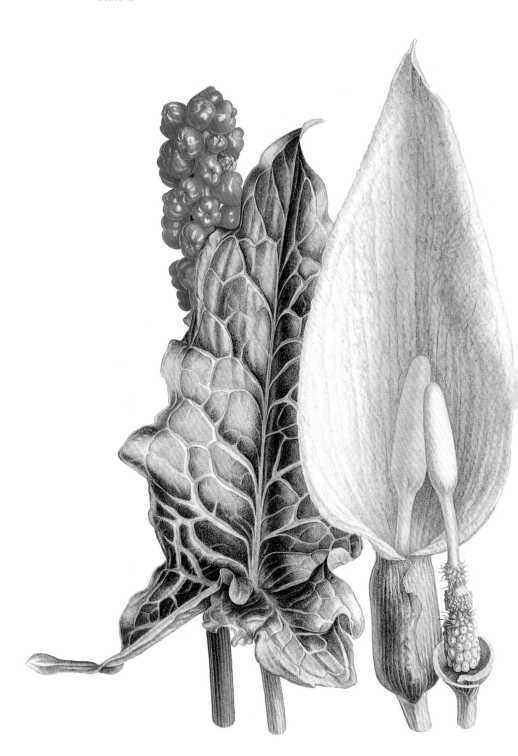

Arum italicum subsp. *italicum*

PANDORA SELLARS

first year. The pots should not be allowed to dry out as this encourages the plants to become dormant. When the leaves start to yellow the watering should be cut back but not stopped. When dormant, the tubers should be treated in the same way as mature plants. It is best to repot the tubers, about three to a 10 cm pot, into fresh compost at the time when the rest of the collection is repotted. The seedlings should now be treated as mature plants. Those species destined for culture outdoors or in frames should be kept in pots for three growth seasons before planting. Any that are intended for glasshouse culture can be planted at the end of their first season.

PESTS AND DISEASES

Arum plants are generally robust and if grown well do not succumb to pests and diseases as readily as many 'bulbous' plants. However, they are not entirely trouble-free, and severe attacks can weaken a plant.

Aphids are the most troublesome pest, infesting and causing distortion of newly emerging leaves and inflorescences. Fortunately aphids are easily controlled either with contact or systemic pesticides. If an attack is particularly severe it is best to use a faster-acting contact pesticide first, followed by a slower-acting, but longer-lasting, systemic one.

Red spider mite is a tenacious pest and far more difficult to control, but luckily its appearance is less frequent than that of aphids. Much has been written about keeping the atmosphere damp to control red spider, but in my experience this is ineffective. If infestations are slight they can be dealt with by spraying the undersides of the leaves with a fairly coarse jet of water. However, if the infestation is severe, with extensive webs on the leaves, chemical means will have to be employed. Red spider builds up resistance to chemicals and so it is wise to use a sequence of at least three types of spray.

Slugs and snails are more of a problem in frames or outdoors than under glass. Despite the toxic nature of all parts of *Arum* to mammals, slugs and snails devour both new shoots and mature leaves. Although there are now numerous slug baits, the most effective method of control is manual removal at night. If this is not possible the new micro-pellets available can be effective. Care should be taken when scattering the bait so that the pellets do not lodge in the leaf-axils where they can decompose when moist and cause rotting of the leaf tissue.

On the whole, diseases cause problems only rarely in cultivated collections. Severe overwatering, or too much moisture when the plants are dormant, can lead to wet rot of the tubers. With dormant tubers, if caught in time, the rotten areas can be cut away and the tuber left out for a couple of days to dry off before repotting into almost dry compost. Invariably wet rot of growing plants is first detected by flaccid leaves and slimy petioles, by which time it is too late to do anything to save the affected tuber. Remove the rotted plant and repot any unaffected tubers into fresh compost, disturbing them as little as possible. *Arum* leaves are rarely affected by fungus diseases, but botrytis can attack the leaves if the glasshouse or frame remains very humid for a long time, e.g. during prolonged foggy weather.

Once again arums are relatively trouble-free where viruses are concerned. Plants will rarely show signs of a virus attack if they are growing strongly. Sickly plants, especially where the roots have been damaged through overwatering, may show signs of Tobacco Mosaic Virus, with distorted, yellow-marbled leaves and small, malformed inflorescences. It is a good policy to destroy any plants that display such symptoms to prevent spread of the virus to healthy plants. If virus is suspected in a collection all possible measures should be taken to control pests such as aphids which can transfer the virus to other, healthy, plants.

TAXONOMY

SUPRAGENERIC CLASSIFICATION

Arum belongs to the subtribe *Arinae*, which is a member of the tribe *Areae* in the subfamily *Aroideae* (Engler, 1920; Bogner, 1978; Bogner & Nicolson, 1991). Within the same tribe are the following subtribes: *Arisarinae* Schott, of which *Arisarum* Targ.-Tozz. is the only genus; *Arisaematinae* Engler, containing only *Arisaema* Martius; *Pinellinae* Schott (*Atherurinae* in Bogner, 1978; Bogner & Nicholson, 1991) which contains just *Pinellia* Tenore. In comparison, *Arinae* consists of *Arum* L., *Biarum* Schott, *Dracunculus* Schott, *Helicodiceros* Schott, *Eminium* (Blume) Schott, *Sauromatum* Schott, *Lazarum* A. Hay, *Theriophonum* Blume and *Typhonium* Schott. In my opinion the genus closest to *Arum* in the Mediterranean is *Eminium*.

The primary feature used to differentiate the genera of the *Arinae* is placentation. In this respect, *Arum* with its single, parietal placenta, is unique in the subtribe.

The genera in the subtribe are distinguished as follows:

1. Placentation parietal **Arum**
   Placentation apical and basal, or basal 2

2. Placentation basal 3
   Placentation apical and basal 7

3. Spathe-tube septate **Lazarum**
   Spathe-tube not septate 4

4. Ovaries 1-ovulate; stigma borne on ± distinctly narrowed style
   Biarum
   Ovaries 2- or 3-ovulate; stigma sessile 5

5. Spathe-tube persistent **Typhonium**
   Spathe-tube withering and eventually deciduous 6

6. Pistillodes clavate **Sauromatum**
   Pistillodes subulate **Eminium**

7. Staminate and pistillate flower-zone contiguous **Dracunculus**
   Staminate and pistillate flower-zones separated, usually with well-developed pistillodes between the zones 8

51

8. Spadix-appendix with numerous hair-like staminodes; leaves
   helicoid-pedatisect **Helicodiceros**
   Spadix-appendix smooth; leaves variously shaped but not as above
   Theriophonum

The Genus Arum

Arum Linnaeus, Gen. Pl., 277 (1737), Sp. Pl., 966 (1753); Schott in
Schott & Endlicher, Melet. Bot., 17 (1832); Blume, Rumphia 1:
116–20 (1836); Endlicher, Gen. Plantarum 1, 3: 235 (1837); Schott,
Syn. Aroid., 9–16 (1856) & Gen. Aroid., t.12, 13 (1858) & Prodr. Syst.
Aroid., 73–102 (1860); Ender, Index Aroid., 22–28 (1864); Pfeiffer,
Nomen. Botanicus 1(1): 283–4 (1873); Engler in A. & C. DC.,
Monogr. Phan. 2: 580–97 (1879) & in Engler & Prantl, Nat. Pflanzen-
fam. 2, 3: 147 (1889); Hruby in Bull. Soc. Bot. Genève 4: 113–60,
330–71 (1912); Engler, Pflanzenr. 73 (IV. 23F): 67–99 (1920). Type:
A. maculatum L.

DESCRIPTION. *Perennial tuberous herbs. Tubers* discoid or rhizomatous. *Roots*
annual, cylindric, growing from the base of the growth point; contractile
roots thickened, simple; feeding roots slender to very slender, ± simple.
Vegetative shoot annual, emerging from early autumn to late winter, base
enclosed by 1–4 fleshy to subfleshy, later papery cataphylls. *Leaves* few to
many, ± erect, petiolate, petioles free to moderately clasping, terete to
D-shaped in cross-section, furnished with a closed wing-like or open sheath
basally; leaf-blade cordate to sagittate or hastate, apex acute to obtuse,
margins entire, posterior lobes well defined to (rarely) almost absent, main
veins indistinct to sunken above, ± prominent beneath. *Inflorescence* sessile to
long-pedunculate, produced at the beginning or end of the growing season,
emerging from the sheath of the terminal leaf-petiole (subgenus *Arum*) or
from 2 or 3 cataphylls apically from the previous season's growth (subgenus
Gymnomesium). *Spathe* consisting of a well-defined tube and limb; spathe-tube
oblong-cylindric to somewhat ventricose, ± constricted apically, more rarely
open and goblet-like, margins free; spathe-limb linear-lanceolate, elliptic or
ovate-elliptic, erect, cucullate, recurved or flopping forward, apex acute to
obtuse. *Spadix* much shorter than to exceeding the spathe, appendix cylindric
to clavate, sometimes massive, long-stipitate to sessile, ± straight, erect,
smooth, apex subacute to obtuse, strongly foetid, sweetly scented or scentless.
*Staminodes** contiguous with the staminate flowers or separated by a naked

*See chapter on morphology (p. 24) for staminode and pistillode distinction.

interstice, staminodes usually well developed, rarely much reduced or absent, filiform to subulate, simple, reflexed, spreading or suberect, bases globose, compressed-globose, bulbiform or subtriangular, rarely absent, surface smooth to verrucate. *Staminate flowers* crowded together in a cylindric, oblong or globose zone, sessile, free, each consisting of 2 to 4 anthers, connective very narrow to ± absent, never prominent, each theca opening by a longitudinal slit (subgenus *Arum*) or a subapical pore (subgenus *Gymnomesium*); pollen free, exine spinulose, very rarely scabrose. *Pistillodes** contiguous with the pistillate flowers or separated by a naked interstice, well developed to absent, filiform, aristate or subulate, simple, reflexed, spreading or suberect, bases globose, compressed-globose, bulbiform or compressed-triangular, rarely absent, surface smooth to verrucate. *Pistillate flowers* crowded together in a cylindric zone at the base of the spadix, each consisting of a 1-loculate, multi-ovulate ovary with a hemispherical, sessile, papillate stigma, which exudes a droplet when withered; ovules orthotropous, placentation parietal. *Infructescence* a cylindric cluster of juicy, few-seeded, pyriform to globose, glossy berries, stigmatic remains apical, sunken. *Seeds* moderately large, ovoid to globose, testa leathery, reticulate, endosperm copious, starchy, embryo straight.

INFRAGENERIC CLASSIFICATION

The infrageneric classification of *Arum* has been investigated by several authors in the past, resulting in a number of different classifications. The most recent (Boyce, 1989) is that on which the present account is based.

The first major attempt to define and restrict the limits of the genus was that of Schott (1832). He removed many of the Linnaean elements from the genus, using these to form the basis for several new genera. Schott's early work set the stage for Blume (1836), who divided *Arum* into two sections. Blume's concept of *Arum* was somewhat wider than is currently recognized, and included species now belonging to *Eminium* and *Peltandra* Rafin. As early as 1855, Schott recognized that *A. pictum* displayed features such as autumn flowering and no pistillodes, which suggested that it was perhaps misplaced in *Arum* as circumscribed at the time. Accordingly he proposed the establishment of a new genus, *Gymnomesium*, to accommodate it (later reduced to infra-generic rank – see species treatment p. 170).

Schott (1856) made no attempt at an infrageneric classification, the arrangement apparently being based on the overall similarity between the taxa.

Schott (1860) placed great emphasis on geographical distribution in grouping the species, whilst giving lower priority to morphological characteristics. This resulted in sections and subsections composed of taxa now regarded as only distantly related. Schott emphasized tuber structure as a basis for sectional distinctions, with peduncle length and the presence or absence of an appendix-stipe used to define the subsections.

While Engler (1879, 1889) accepted, on a modified basis, Schott's (1860) classification, in *Das Pflanzenreich* (Engler, 1920) he opted for a radically different treatment. This classification is based primarily on sterile flower morphology, with emphasis on the shape of the stami-nodes and pistillodes, and the degree of sculpturing on their ex-panded bases.

Hruby (1912) presented a system based on the supposed phylo-genetic relationships of the species. He proposed three 'infra-glacial' evolutionary groups, derived from a hypothetical 'pre-glacial *Arum*'. The resultant groups are based upon *A. maculatum, A. orientale* and *A. dioscoridis* and are distinguished by features of spathe shape and spadix morphology.

My new classification (Boyce, 1989 – see p. 55) combines much from earlier treatments, especially those of Schott (1860) and Engler (1920). The removal of *A. pictum* into a new subgenus, *Gymnomesium*, is based on the timing of the flowering period and details of the sterile flowers, leaves and petiole-sheaths. At section level I have placed importance on tuber shape (discoid or rhizomatous), while the mode of inflorescence presentation ('flag' or 'cryptic'), whether the infloresc-ences are scented or odourless, the shape of the spadix-appendix and the sterile flower structure are treated as critical characters at subsec-tional level.

I feel that the inclusion of data relating to the physical processes of reproduction is important. The success of a species in the wild is directly linked to its ability to attract pollinators. In the past this type of data has not been included in that used to classify *Arum* and its addition to the present treatment has been a major contributing factor in delimiting the taxa.

SYNOPSIS OF THE GENUS

1. Subgenus *Arum* – see p. 59

   I. Section *Arum* – see p. 60
     1. *A. maculatum*
     2. *A. byzantinum*
     3. *A. italicum*
     4. *A. concinnatum*

   II. Section *Dioscoridea* – see p. 84
     a. Subsection *Alpina* – see p. 85
       5. *A. alpinum*
     b. Subsection *Dischroochiton* – see p. 90
       6. *A. orientale*
       7. *A. gratum*
       8. *A. lucanum*
       9. *A. apulum*
       10. *A. nigrum*
       11. *A. cyrenaicum*
       12. *A. purpureospathum*
       13. *A. balansanum*
       14. *A. hainesii*
       15. *A. elongatum*
     c. Subsection *Tenuifila* – see p. 129
       16. *A. rupicola*
       17. *A. jacquemontii*
       18. *A. korolkowii*
     d. Subsection *Hygrophila* – see p. 142
       19. *A. euxinum*
       20. *A. hygrophilum*
     e. Subsection *Poeciloporphyochiton* – see p. 150
       21. *A dioscoridis*
       22. *A. palaestinum*
     f. Subsection *Cretica* – see p. 162
       23. *A. idaeum*
       24. *A. creticum*

2. Subgenus *Gymnomesium* – see p. 169
     25. *A. pictum*

Key to the Subgenera

1. Plant flowering in the spring or early summer, after leaf emergence; inflorescence situated above ground level, very rarely at ground level (*A. gratum*), spathe-tube fully exposed, no cataphylls present at inflorescence base; peduncles extending markedly during maturation of infructescence in those species with cryptic inflorescences; staminodes and pistillodes both present (except in subsection *Cretica* where they are both absent), bristles filiform to subulate, ± slender; petioles with closed triangular sheaths, sheath margins wing-like, concealing the sheath interior **1.** subgenus **Arum**
   Plant flowering in the autumn, before or with leaf emergence; inflorescence situated at ground level, spathe-tube partially buried and enveloped by 2 or 3 triangular, subfleshy cataphylls; peduncles barely extending during maturation of infructescence; staminodes present, bristles subulate, thick; pistillodes absent; petioles with open, triangular sheaths, sheath margins not wing-like, sheath interior thus exposed
   2. subgenus **Gymnomesium**

Key to the Sections and Subsections

1. Rootstock consisting of a horizontal rhizomatous tuber with lateral adventitious shoots forming offsets which later become independent; established plants forming extensive spreading colonies **i.** sect. **Arum**
   Rootstock consisting of a vertically or horizontally orientated discoid tuber with peripheral adventitious shoots which sometimes form independent plants; established plants forming congested, compact colonies
   (**ii.** sect. **Dioscoridea**) 2

2. Spadix-appendix long-stipitate 3
   Spadix-appendix either short-stipitate, or sessile 4

3. Peduncles longer than the petioles; inflorescence scentless; both staminodes and pistillodes with long, filiform, semi-rigid bristles
   a. subsect. **Alpina**
   Peduncles shorter than the petioles; inflorescence with foetid, oily or sweet, fermenting odour; pistillodes with long, slender-filiform, flexuous bristles, staminodes either similar or with short, aristate, stiff bristles **b.** subsect. **Dischroochiton**

4. Staminodes and pistillodes well developed 5
   Staminodes and pistillodes absent or barely developed
   f. subsect. **Cretica**

5. Spadix-appendix stipitate, more than 5 mm in diameter, spathe-tube interior white or stained with purple in the upper portion, rarely entirely purple   6

   Spadix-appendix not stipitate, less than 4 mm in diameter, spathe-tube interior wholly purple   **d.** subsect. **Hygrophila**

6. Peduncles ± equal to or exceeding the petioles; bristles of staminodes and pistillodes filiform, flexuous; inflorescence scentless

    c. subsect. **Tenuifila**

   Peduncles shorter than the petioles, occasionally ± absent; bristles of staminodes and pistillodes subulate, stiff; inflorescence with strong odour, foetid or smelling of fermenting apples, very rarely scentless

    e. subsect. **Poeciloporphyrochiton**

Key to the Species

1. Tuber rhizomatous   2
   Tuber discoid   5

2. Spadix-appendix massively to stoutly clavate-cylindric, subequal to more than ½ as long as spathe-limb   **4. A. concinnatum**
   Spadix-appendix ± slender-clavate, ¼–½ as long as spathe-limb   3

3. Staminate flowers yellow before anthesis   **3. A. italicum**
   Staminate flowers purple before anthesis   4

4. Spathe-limb pale green, ± stained with brownish purple; leaves weakly hastate (NW Turkey)   **2. A. byzantinum**
   Spathe-limb usually greenish white; leaves sagittate-hastate (throughout Europe)   **1. A. maculatum**

5. Pistillodes and/or staminodes present   6
   Pistillodes and staminodes usually absent   24

6. Plant flowering in autumn; staminodes present, pistillodes absent or vestigial   **25. A. pictum**
   Plant flowering in spring to early summer; staminodes and pistillodes present   7

7. Spathe-limb usually blotched and spotted with purple on inner surface, inflorescence strongly foetid, very rarely odourless   **21. A. dioscoridis**
   Spathe-limb not marked on inner surface or, if markings present, then inflorescence smelling oily   8

8. Bristles of staminodes and pistillodes subulate   9
   Bristles of staminodes and pistillodes filiform or subulate   10

9. Spathe-limb broadly elliptic; spadix-appendix clavate to stoutly cylindric, long-stipitate, *c.* ½ as long as spathe   **10. A. nigrum**
Spathe-limb lanceolate; spadix-appendix stoutly cylindric, short-stipitate, subequal to more than ½ as long as spathe-limb   **22. A. palaestinum**

10. Spathe-tube distinctly bicoloured on inner surface, purple above, pale green to white below   11
Spathe-tube not bicoloured on inner surface   15

11. Spadix-appendix strongly clavate; inflorescence with a sweet-oily odour
    7. A. gratum
Spadix-appendix stoutly to slender-cylindric; inflorescence with a foetid or sweet, fermenting odour   12

12. Spadix-appendix stoutly cylindric, subequal to spathe-limb, if slender then spathe-limb interior crimson   **15. A. elongatum**
Spadix-appendix slender-cylindric, up to ¾ as long as spathe-limb; spathe-limb interior never crimson   13

13. Spathe-limb pale green suffused with pale to mid-purple on inner surface   14
Spathe-limb rosy purple to dark purple on inner surface, often paler towards the middle   **11. A. cyrenaicum**

14. Spathe-limb evenly suffused with pale purple on inner surface; ovaries stained purple apically; staminodes in 2 whorls, pistillodes in 3 or 4 whorls   **6. A. orientale**
Spathe-limb margins and apex mid-green, centre purple on inner surface; ovaries concolorous pale green; staminodes in 3 or 4 whorls, pistillodes in 1 or 2 whorls   **9. A. apulum**

15. Spathe-tube white or greenish white inside, sometimes flushed with pale purple above and along the margin   16
Spathe-tube deep purple inside   20

16. Inflorescence borne above the leaves or equal to them   17
Inflorescence borne beneath the leaves   22

17. Spathe-limb elliptic-lanceolate; spadix-appendix generally slender long-stipitate, cylindric to clavate   **5. A. alpinum**
Spathe-limb lanceolate to linear-lanceolate; spadix-appendix generally stout, stipitate or stalkless, cylindric   18

18. Spathe-limb green on inner surface   **18. A. korolkowii**
Spathe-limb purple, or rarely greenish white with a narrow purple border on inner surface   19

19. Spadix-appendix cylindric, tapering basally, stalkless; pistillodes and staminode bases purple **17. A. jacquemontii**
    Spadix-appendix cylindric to conic-cylindric, sometimes massively so, short-stipitate; pistillode and staminode bases off-white
    16. A. rupicola

20. Spathe-limb deep purple inside **12. A. purpureospathum**
    Spathe-limb ± pale green inside 21

21. Inflorescence borne beneath the leaves; spathe-limb with a 1–1.5 mm wide purple border; leaves with basal lobes more than ⅓ as long as blade **20. A. hygrophilum**
    Inflorescence borne above the leaves; spathe-limb with a 2.5–3 mm wide border; leaves with basal lobes less than ¼ as long as blade
    19. A. euxinum

22. Spadix-appendix very slender, subequal to longer than spathe-limb
    8. A. lucanum
    Spadix-appendix stout, shorter than spathe-limb 23

23. Leaf width *c*. ⅔ of leaf length; spathe-limb pale green to purple on inner surface, pale green to pale purple on outer surface; spadix-appendix purple **13. A. balansanum**
    Leaf width *c*. ¾ of leaf length; spathe-limb pale green on both surfaces; spadix-appendix pale brown **14. A. hainesii**

24. Spathe cream to yellow, limb reflexing at maturity; spadix-appendix mid-yellow to dark yellow, sweetly scented **24. A. creticum**
    Spathe white, limb erect and cucullate at maturity; spadix-appendix deep purple, scentless **23. A. idaeum**

1. Subgenus Arum

Arum subgenus **Arum**
Arum subgenus '*Euarum*' Engler in Engler & Prantl, Nat. Pflanzenfam. 2, 3: 147 (1889), *nom. inval.* (Art. 21.3).

Description as in the key to the subgenera (p. 56).

I. Section Arum

Arum section **Arum**

Arum subsection *Chlorochiton* Schott, Prodr. Syn. Aroid., 74 (1860). Lectotype: *A. italicum* Miller (selected by Boyce in Kew Bull. 44: 390, 1989).

Arum section *'Euarum'* Engler in A. & C. DC., Monogr. Phan. 2: 583 (1879), *nom. inval.* (Art. 21.3).

Arum subsection *Ootuberosae* Engler, *op. cit.*, 591. Lectotype: *A. italicum* Miller (selected by Boyce in Kew Bull. 44: 390, 1989).

Arum [infragen. group] *'Ootuberosae'* Engler, Nat. Pflanzenfam. 2, 3: 147 (1889), rankless taxon (see Boyce, 1989).

Description as in the key to the sections and subsections (p. 56).

1. ARUM MACULATUM

The LORDS AND LADIES of our hedgerows will need no introduction to most readers, enlivening the wayside with its glossy, deep green foliage in spring and brilliant, orange-red pokers of ripe fruit in the late summer. It has, by and large, been overlooked by gardeners, which is a great pity since *A. maculatum* is not only easy to grow but is also a first-rate, although somewhat invasive, garden plant, offering attractive foliage, flowers and fruit. Although deep green is the usual leaf colour, forms with black-spotted foliage are quite frequent. Similarly the pale greenish white of the spathe is often covered irregularly with purple-black spots and patches, or the margins and limb may be stained purple, dull pink or yellow. Apart from colour differences, the leaf shape and size are also highly variable, as are the spathe dimensions.

Arum maculatum has been the subject of numerous scientific papers, and the wide range of variation encountered in the species has led to a multitude of scientific names. The problem is compounded by 'new' taxa being described from single collections originating within a mixed population showing wider variation. An indication of the variability of *A. maculatum* can be gained by sowing seed collected from one fruiting head gathered from an open-pollinated population and observing the resulting seedlings. A wide range of leaf shape and coloration will be seen and if the plants are grown on to flowering size a similar range of inflorescence shape, size and colour will be observed.

Arum maculatum L., Sp. Pl., 966 (1753); Schott, Syn. Aroid., 11 (1856) & Prodr. Syst. Aroid., 92 (1860); Engler in A. & C. DC., Monogr. Phan. 2: 593 (1879); Hruby in Bull. Soc. Bot. Genève 4: 12 (1912) *pro parte*; Engler, Pflanzenr. 73 (IV. 23F): 87 (1920). Type: southern Europe (Herb. Linn. 1078/8 [LINN!]; syntype UP! (microfiche): lectotype selected here). The specimen in the Linnaean Herbarium, London, is complete whereas that in Uppsala lacks most of the spadix. Thus the Linnaean Herbarium specimen is more suitable as the lectotype.

A. vulgare Lam., Fl. Fr. 3: 537 (1778). Type: not designated.

A. pyrenaeum Dufour in Lap., Hist. Abr. Phyt. Pyr. Suppl., 14 (1818). Type: Pyrenees, sur le base ombragée des rochers qui bordent le chemin di Lac Gaube, assez près de Cauterets, *Dufour* s.n. (holotype not traced, ?P).

A. maculatum L. var. *immaculatum* Reichb., Fl. Germ. Excurs., 10 (1830). Type: not designated.

A. maculatum L. var. *immaculatum* Mutel, Fl. Fr. 3: 339 (1836). Type: not designated.

A. immaculatum (Reichb.) Schott, Prodr. Syst. Aroid., 93 (1860).

A. malyi Schott, *loc. cit.* Type: Yugoslavia, Montes nigri, Dalmatiae vicini, 1837, *Maly* s.n. (holotype W, destroyed; lectotype selected here: Schott Icones Aroideae no. 1330, W!).

A. zelebori Schott, *op. cit.*, 94. Type: Yugoslavia, Bosnia, *Zelebor* s.n. (holotype W, destroyed; lectotype selected here: Schott Icones Aroideae no. 1364, W!).

[*A. orientale* sensu Besser in Knapp., Planzen. a.d. Burkowina 78 (1874), *non* Bieb. (1808).]

A. trapezuntinum Schott ex Engler in A. & C. DC., Monogr. Phan. 2: 592 (1879). Type: not cited.

[*A. maculatum* L. forma '*vulgaris immaculata*' Engler, *op. cit.*, 594.]

[*A. maculatum* L. forma '*vulgaris maculata*' Engler, *op. cit.*, 595.]

A. maculatum L. subsp. *pyrenaeum* (Dufour) Nyman, Consp. Fl. Europ., 755 (1882).

A. maculatum L. var. *tetrelii* Corbière, Fl. Norm., 2nd Suppl. (1898). Type (France) Dep. Eure, Sainte-Barbe près des Louviers, *Tetrel* s.n. (holotype P!).

A. maculatum L. var. *zelebori* (Schott) Beck. v. Mannag., Flora Bosne 2: 58 (1903).

[*A. albispathum* sensu Hruby in Bull. Soc. Bot. Genève 4: 150 (1912), *pro parte.*]

A. italicum Miller var. *amoenum* Engler, Pflanzenr. 73 (IV. 23F): 86 (1920). Type: (Turkey) Trapezunt in montosis vall. Dermendere, 25 April 1890, *Sintenis* 2064 (holotype B, destroyed; isotypes K! LD, P! WU).

A. maculatum L. var. *vulgare* (Lam.) Engler, *op. cit.*, 88.

A. maculatum L. var. *vulgare* (Lam.) Engler subvar. *eumaculatum* Engler, *loc. cit.*, *nom. illeg.*

A. maculatum L. var. *vulgare* (Lam.) Engler subvar. *immaculatum* (Mutel) Engler, *loc. cit.*

A. maculatum L. var. *vulgare* (Lam.) Engler subvar. *pyrenaeum* (Dufour) Engler, *op. cit.*, 91.

A. maculatum L. var. *vulgare* (Lam.) Engler subvar. *roseum* Gremblich ex Engler, *loc. cit.* Type: (Italy) southern Alps, Valle Bosiana am Monte Baldo, *Pollini* s.n. (holotype B, destroyed).

A. maculatum L. var. *angustatum* Engler subvar. *malyi* (Schott) Engler, *op. cit.*, 93.

A. maculatum L. var. *angustatum* Engler forma *scolopendriforme* Priszter ex Horvat in Borbásia 9: 129 (1949). Type: Hungary: Pécs, Mecsek, Kisrét, 1948, *Priszter* s.n. (holotype not traced).

[*A. maculatum* L. forma *flavescens* Melzer ex Janchen, Cat. Fl. Austr. 1: 877 (1960), *nom. nud.*]

A. maculatum L. subsp. *maculatum* var. *immaculatum* Reichb. forma *flavescens* Melzer ex H. Riedl in Phyton 12 (1–4): 166 (1967), *nom. illeg.*

A. maculatum L. subsp. *maculatum* var. *immaculatum* Reichb. forma *roseum* (Gremblich ex Engler) H. Riedl, *loc. cit.*

A. maculatum L. var. *karpatii* Terpó in Bot. Közlem. 58, 3: 157 (1971). Type: Hungary, inter oppidum Mosonmagyaróvár et Halaszi, 12 May 1969, *Czimber, Erdös & Terpó*, 18234 (holotype KEH).

A. maculatum L. var. *maculatum* forma *spathulatum* Terpó, *loc. cit.* Type: Hungary, inter oppidum Mosonmagyaróvár et Kimle, 1969, *Terpó-Pomogyi & Terpó*, 14482 (holotype KEH).

A. maculatum L. var. *maculatum* forma *tetrelii* (Corbière) Terpó, *op. cit.*, 160.

A. maculatum L. subsp. *maculatum* var. *immaculatum* forma *flavescens* Melzer ex H. Riedl in Hegi, Ill. Fl. von Mitt.-Eur. (edn.2) 12:

331 (1980). Type: Austria, Styria australis prope Mureck, in silvis secus flumen Mur, 30 April 1968, *Riedl* s.n. (lectotype designated by Riedl, *loc. cit.*, W).

A. orientale Bieb. subsp. *amoenum* (Engler) R. Mill in Notes Roy. Bot. Gard. Edinb. 41: 47 (1983).

[*A. heldreichii* Orph. *in sched. nom. nud.*]

DESCRIPTION. *Tuberous herb* sprouting in late winter to early spring from a rhizomatous tuber 3–6 cm long, 2–2.5 cm thick. *Petiole* terete to D-shaped in cross-section, 9–53 cm long, 6–11 mm wide, mid-green to deep green. *Leaf-blade* sagittate-hastate to oblong-hastate or oblong-lanceolate-hastate, apex acute to obtuse, 7–27 cm long, 3.5–19 cm wide, mid-green to deep green, often lightly to heavily marked with jagged, purple-black spots and patches, these often bullate. *Inflorescence* smelling moderately of sour urine. *Peduncle* much shorter than to equalling the leaves, terete, 4–26 cm long, 6–8 mm wide, mid-green to deep green. *Spathe* 6.5–27 cm long, spathe-tube ovoid-oblong, 1.5–5 cm long, 1.2.5 cm wide, moderately to rather strongly constricted apically, exterior pale to mid-green, interior greenish white, usually with a *c.* 5 mm wide purple band around the middle, more rarely the

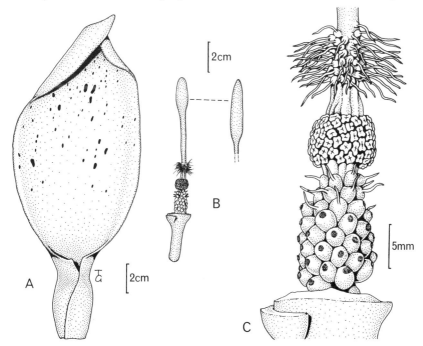

Arum maculatum. **A**, spathe; **B**, spadix, showing variation in shape and size; **C**, base of spadix.

63

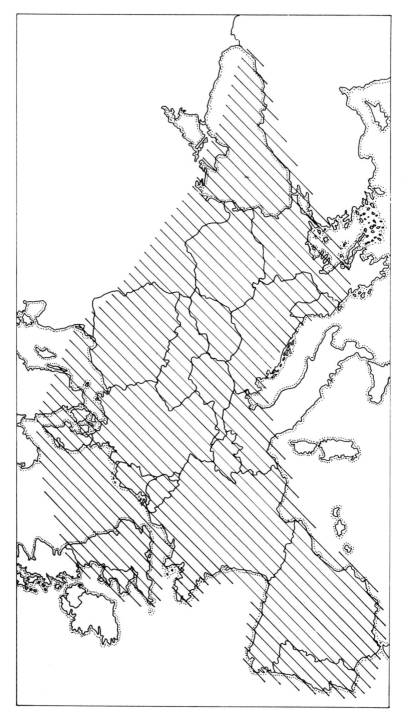

Map 1. Distribution of *Arum maculatum.*

Plate 3

Arum concinnatum

ANN FARRER

Plate 4

Arum alpinum

ANN FARRER

tube apex may be suffused with purple within; spathe-limb elliptic-ovate to lanceolate-elliptic, or narrowly lanceolate, 5–22 cm long, 3–12 cm wide, erect, acuminate to acute, the tip tending to droop as the inflorescence ages, externally pale to mid-green, the margins occasionally suffused with purple, rarely the whole exterior mid-purple, internally greenish white to yellowish green, often similarly spotted to the foliage, more rarely pale yellow or flushed with pink to mid-purple, very rarely wholly mid-purple. *Spadix* ⅓–½ as long as the spathe-limb, 4–14 cm in total length; appendix slender-clavate to subcylindric, rarely broadly clavate or conical, long-stipitate, 2.5–9 cm long, 2.5–9 mm wide, deep purple to pale yellow, more rarely dull brown, stipe usually darker. *Staminodes* in 5 or 6 whorls forming a zone 3–9 mm long; bristles filiform, flexuous, 5–6 mm long, purple to violet; bases conic, weakly verrucate, pale yellow. *Interstices*: upper 0–3 mm long with some rudimentary staminode bases, pale cream; lower similar. *Staminate flowers* in an oblong to quadrate zone 1.5–7 mm long, 2.7–5 mm wide, anthers and connectives dark to mid-purple. *Pistillodes* in 1–3 whorls forming a zone 2.5–7 mm long; bristles filiform to aristate, flexuous, 2.5–3 mm long, purple to violet; bases bulbiform to compressed-triangular, ± smooth, pale yellow. *Pistillate flowers* in a cylindric to globose-cylindric cluster 8–21 mm long; ovaries ellipsoid-oblong, 2–3.5 mm long, cream to very pale greenish yellow, purple apically, stigma white. *Fruiting spike* cylindric to oblong-cylindric, 2.5–5 cm long, 1.5–2 cm wide; berries oblong-ovoid, 4–11 mm long, 3.5–5 mm wide. *Germination* hypogeal.

ILLUSTRATIONS. PLATE 1. Ross-Craig, Draw. Brit. Pl. 30: pl.39 (1973).

FLOWERING PERIOD. Mid-April to late May, with inflorescences opening sporadically into early June.

HABITAT. Open deciduous woodland, forest edges, hedgerows; waste-land in ruderal habitats; sea-level to 1,300 m.

DISTRIBUTION. Throughout Europe, from NW Spain to the Caucasus, and from S Sweden to N Greece. Although occurring in Scandinavia, many of the records from this region are referable to *A. alpinum*. MAP 1, p. 64.

2. ARUM BYZANTINUM

This small plant, restricted to western Turkey, has been much confused with the larger and more widespread *A. concinnatum*. The confusion seems to stem from Schott's statement (1857b) that *A. byzantinum* was described from Cretan material. However, a careful check of the relevant literature shows that this is not the case and *A. byzantinum* is, in fact, absent from Crete. Blume (1836) published the name *A. byzantinum* with nothing more than a reference to Clusius (1601), stating that the plant was poorly known to him and implying that he intended *A. byzantinum* to be based on the illustration published by Clusius. Schott redescribed *A. byzantinum* in 1857 from a specimen flowering at Schönbrunn, in Vienna. Unfortunately, Schott based his description on material originating from Crete rather than Turkey. His reference to grey-green leaf markings suggests that the collection he used was *A. concinnatum*, and certainly the illustrations in the *Icones Aroidearum* identified as *A. byzantinum* are referable to *A. concinnatum*. Comparison of *A. concinnatum* to the leaves illustrated in Clusius' work clearly demonstrate that they are not the same species.

Arum byzantinum is similar to both *A. italicum* and *A. maculatum*. From the former it is distinguishable by its brownish purple-stained spathes, narrower, purple spadix-appendix and purple pistillodes, staminodes and staminate flowers. It differs from *A. maculatum* by the verrucate bases of the sterile flowers, the greenish white spathe-tube interior, divergent posterior leaf-lobes and smaller overall size. The three species are all closely allied and intermediates between this group and the distinct *A. concinnatum* are occasionally found. However, the four species belonging to section *Arum* are usually readily separable.

At present *A. byzantinum* is infrequently seen in cultivation, which is regrettable since it is quite hardy and easily grown in a damp, shady spot. However, it is prone to being swamped by larger, more vigorous plants and so a little care about positioning is required. If plants of *A. byzantinum* are purchased, it is important that the plants are seen in flower, since purchased material of *A. byzantinum* often turns out to be *A. concinnatum*.

Arum byzantinum Blume, Rumphia 1: 121 (1836); Schott, Syn. Aroid., 15 (1856) & Prodr. Syst. Aroid., 86 (1860); Hruby in Bull. Soc. Bot. Genève 4: 135, t.14 (1912). Type: Illustration in Clusius, Rar. Pl. Hist. Lib. 4: 73, t.49 (1601!).

A. *italicum* Miller var. *byzantinum* (Blume) Engler in A. & C. DC., Monogr. Phan. 2: 593 (1879) & in Engler, Pflanzenr. 73 (IV. 23F): 86 (1920).

A. *italicum* Miller subsp. *byzantinum* (Blume) Nyman, Consp. Fl. Europ., 755 (1882).

A. *italicum* Miller subsp. *byzantinum* (Blume) Richter, Pl. Europ. 1: 173 (1890), *comb. illeg.*

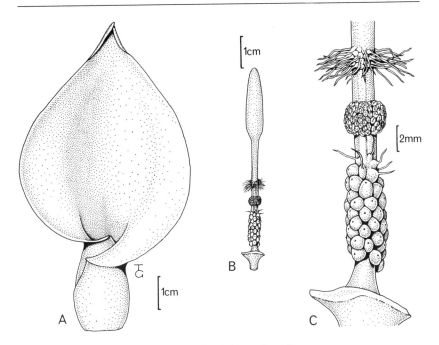

Arum byzantinum. A, spathe; **B**, spadix; **C**, base of spadix.

DESCRIPTION. *Tuberous herb* sprouting in late autumn from a rhizomatous tuber 5–7 cm long, 1.5–2.5 cm thick. *Petiole* terete, 13–55 cm long, 3–5 mm wide, dull mid-green, tinged and obscurely striped with purple for at least some of its length. *Leaf-blade* oblong-hastate to triangular, apex acute to obtuse or rounded, 12–25 cm long, 7–18 cm wide, dark green, occasionally with sparse, purple-black spotting. *Inflorescence* smelling weakly of stale urine. *Peduncle* shorter than to subequal to the leaves, 5.5–20 cm long, 3–4 mm wide, terete, dull green, lightly stained with purple below. *Spathe* 8.5–25.5 cm long; spathe-tube ventricose, 2–4.5 cm long, 1.5–2 cm wide, constricted apically, exterior pale green ± stained with brownish purple, interior pale greenish white; spathe-limb narrowly elliptic-lanceolate, 6.5–21 cm long, 1.7–8 cm wide, erect, acute to acuminate, the apical portion drooping as the inflorescence ages, externally pale green with light brownish purple staining, especially towards the margins, internally similarly coloured, but with the staining much more pronounced, particularly along the margins. *Spadix* less then ½ as long as the limb, 4.5–10 cm in total length; appendix slender-clavate, long-stipitate, 2.8–5 cm long, 2–6 (–7) mm wide, purple, the stipe somewhat darker. *Staminodes* in *c.* 3 whorls, forming a zone 2.5–6 mm long; bristles filiform, 2.5–6 mm long, pale purple; bases conic, verrucate, cream. *Interstices*: upper 2–2.5 mm long, ± smooth, cream, lower 0.5–1 mm long, with scattered vestigial sterile flowers, cream. *Staminate flowers* in a ± quadrate zone 1.5–4

67

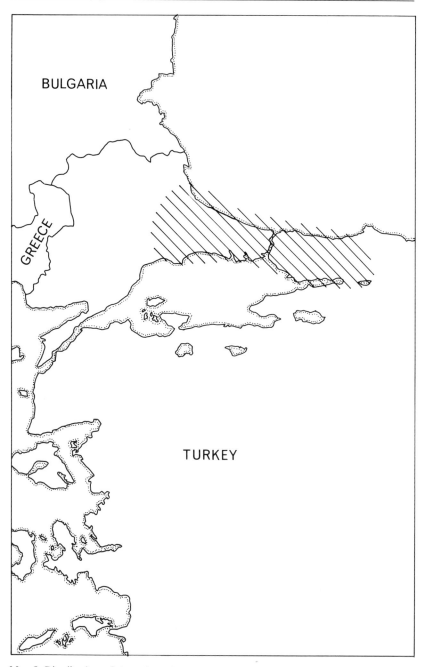

Map 2. Distribution of *Arum byzantinum*.

mm long, 1.5–3 mm wide; anthers purple and connectives dull yellow. *Pistillodes* in *c*. 3 whorls, forming a zone 2.5–4 mm long; bristles filiform, flexuous, 2.5–4 mm long, pale purple; bases laterally compressed-conic, verrucate, cream. *Pistillate flowers* in an oblong-cylindric cluster 3.5–16 mm long; ovaries oblong, truncate apically, 1.5–2.5 mm long, pale yellowish green, stained with purple apically, stigma darker. *Fruiting spike* cylindric, 4.5–7 cm long; berries oblong-ovoid, 3.5–9 mm long, 3.5–4 mm wide. *Germination* unknown.

ILLUSTRATION. Apart from the type citation (Clusius, 1601) I have been unable to locate an illustration of this species.

FLOWERING PERIOD. Late May to early June.

HABITAT. Deciduous woodland, damp banks and hedgerows; sea-level to 800 m.

DISTRIBUTION. NW Turkey (Turkey-in-Europe). MAP 2, p. 68.

3. ARUM ITALICUM

Arum italicum is a well-known species, grown not only for the attractive foliage, but also for the richly coloured berries that are produced in the autumn. It is similar to *A. maculatum* but a number of features, including the different growth period, cream-coloured staminate flowers, distinctly hastate leaves and the generally later flowering period effectively separate the two species. A further difference is that the smell produced by the spadix-appendix of *A. italicum* is far stronger and of longer duration than that produced by *A. maculatum*.

Four subspecies of *A. italicum* are recognized in the present work: subsp. *italicum*, subsp. *albispathum*, subsp. *canariense* and subsp. *neglectum*. Subsp. *canariense*, endemic to the Atlantic Islands, is given subspecific status for the first time.

The typical subspecies occurs from Portugal to the Crimea and from southern England to Morocco. The question as to whether subsp. *italicum* is a British native or merely a garden escape was discussed by Prime (1960). He put forward a convincing argument in favour of the existence of native populations in Hampshire and the Isle of Wight, stating that both localities were well away from possible sources of escaped plants. *Arum italicum* subsp. *italicum* is however widespread on both Jersey and Guernsey and the seed, which is readily eaten by birds, could possibly make the relatively short journey in a bird's stomach.

Subsp. *neglectum*, the so-called RARE LORDS AND LADIES, was first described from Hampshire as *A. italicum* var. *neglectum* by Townsend (1883), although it had been noted in 1854 growing on the Isle of Wight, where it was assumed to be the typical subspecies (Prime, 1960). Townsend's varietal status was retained for over half a century until Ridley (1938) published the result of his extensive research on *A. italicum*, concluding that the Hampshire plant represented a distinct species, *A. neglectum*. Late work by Prime (1961) showed that Ridley perhaps adopted too narrow a view of specific limits. Prime's paper concluded with the proposal that the taxon should be given subspecific status within *A. italicum*. This is accepted in the present work.

Apart from geographical differences, there are a number of morphological features which separate subsp. *italicum* from subsp. *neglectum*. Both begin growth in early autumn, but the emergent leaves of subsp. *neglectum* are broad and blunt with short, slightly divergent or overlapping posterior lobes while those of subsp. *italicum* are narrow and pointed with long, widely divergent posterior lobes. A less reliable character, although still useful, is the leaf colour; subsp. *neglectum* invariably has uniformly deep green leaves, entirely lacking the silver-grey veining typical of subsp. *italicum*. Only rarely do the leaves of subsp. *neglectum* have small purple-black spots.

Ridley (1938) noted that the number of seeds per berry was generally less in subsp. *neglectum* than in subsp. *italicum*, but stated that this feature was not stable.

Arum canariense, described in 1848 from material collected at Palma on Gran Canaria, has long been regarded as synonymous with *A. italicum* subsp. *italicum*. However, Madeiran collections in the herbaria at Edinburgh, Kew and Berlin are notable for their purple spathe-tube interior, depauperate staminodes and dull purple petioles and peduncles. Furthermore the leaves and inflorescences of these plants are considerably more robust than those of mainland populations. The Madeiran plants, along with gatherings of similar material from Gran Canaria and Tenerife, are very striking and obviously distinct from mainland populations of *A. italicum* subsp. *italicum*, and in my opinion merit recognition at subspecific rank as proposed here.

Material from the Crimean Peninsula with particularly large, white spathes has been variously described as *A. albispathum* Steven, *A. italicum* subsp. *albispathum* (Steven ex Ledeb.) Prime and *A. orientale* Bieb. var. *albispathum* (Steven ex Ledeb.) Engler. However, Steven's publication is predated by a description published by Ledebour

(1853) quoting Steven's manuscript name of *A. albispathum*. It is quite possible that Ledebour did not intend his description to validate *A. albispathum*. Nevertheless, Ledebour's publication is effective and valid and thus has priority over that of Steven. Interestingly, Schott (1856) also described *A. albispathum*, quoting Steven's manuscript name but made no reference to Ledebour's work.

In overall appearance *A. albispathum* is quite different to *A. italicum*, with smaller, unmarked, deep green leaves and large, pale spathes. Geographically as well it is discrete from the main Turkish distribution of *A. italicum*. With these factors taken into account the recognition of subsp. *albispathum* seems appropriate.

The attractive foliage of *A. italicum* subsp. *italicum* is one of the main reasons for its popularity, but the distinctness and the type of markings are variable. Undoubtedly the most sought-after plants are those that display heavy silver-grey or creamy white veins. This patterning is particularly striking when the leaves are newly emerged. However, there is a range of leaf pattern, from silvery blotches to purple-black spots and speckles, together with combinations of the two. Occasionally plants with totally deep green leaves may be found which resemble *A. italicum* subsp. *neglectum* except that the leaves are narrow with long, divergent basal lobes. The various colour forms have been given names in the past but the leaf patterning is so variable that the distinctions are meaningless. It should be noted that the epithet 'pictum' has never been published in combination with *A. italicum* at any rank. *Arum italicum* var. *pictum* is thus an invalid name and should be avoided. In addition the use of 'Pictum' to designate cultivar status should be discouraged since not only has it not been published, but it also simply causes confusion between *A. italicum* and *A. pictum*.

In recent years a number of cultivars of *A. italicum* have appeared, e.g. 'Chameleon', 'Tiny' and 'White Winter'. Of these, 'Chameleon' is really rather distinct. It has broadly hastate leaves that are coloured in three shades of green in swirling patterns. It is clearly a selection of subsp. *italicum* and, while only little material is presently available, it promises to be a most useful and attractive garden plant.

Arum besserianum, described by Schott (1858a) has generally been regarded as synonymous with *A. italicum*, but further study is required to establish its true status. Unfortunately, the type description gives no details of tuber shape or inflorescence colour. Terpó (1973) regarded *A. besserianum* as distinct and illustrated his paper with a line drawing depicting a plant with a discoid tuber. He described the spathe-limb as greenish white and the spathe-tube interior as white, features which suggest a link with *A. italicum*. Nevertheless, the elongated spadix-appendix together with the discoid rather than rhizomatous tuber, suggest that *A. besserianum* may be allied to *A. orientale*, or possibly to *A. elongatum*, rather than to *A. italicum*.

Arum italicum Miller, Gard. Dict. (edn.8) no.2 (1768). Schott, Syn. Aroid., 10 (1856) & Prodr. Syst. Aroid., 82 (1860); Engler in A. & C. DC., Monogr. Phan. 2: 591 (1879); Hruby in Bull. Soc. Bot. Genève 4: 128 (1912); Engler, Pflanzenr. 73 (IV. 23F): 82 (1920); Mayo & Meikle in Meikle, Fl. Cyprus 2: 1667 (1985). Type: described from material cultivated at the Chelsea Physic Garden, London (holotype BM–SL!).

DESCRIPTION. *Tuberous herb* sprouting in early autumn or early winter from a rhizomatous tuber 3.5–7.5 cm long, 1.3–3 cm thick. *Petiole* terete to slightly D-shaped in cross-section, 15–35(–40) cm long, 5–9 (–12) mm wide, deep to mid-green, rarely dull purple. *Leaf-blade* narrowly or broadly hastate or sagittate-hastate or ovate-oblong, apex acute to obtuse, 9–35 (–40) cm long, 2–29 cm wide, plain deep green or with primary and main lateral veins slightly to heavily silver-grey, cream or yellowish green, more rarely blade marked with irregular black-purple spots or cloudy silver-grey blotches, or in various shades of green and white, or a combination of any of these. *Inflorescence* smelling strongly of stale urine or occasionally reminiscent of pineapple and citrus. *Peduncle* much shorter than the leaves, terete, 4.6–16 cm long, 6–11 mm wide, pale to mid-green, rarely dull purple. *Spathe* 11–27 (–38) cm long; spathe-tube oblong-ventricose, 3–5(–7) cm long, 1.5–2.5 (–3.5) cm wide, constricted apically, exterior pale to mid-green, sometimes stained brownish purple at the base and along the margins, interior greenish white, sometimes stained with purple apically, rarely entirely purple; spathe-limb elliptic-lanceolate to elliptic-ovate or broadly elliptic, 9–24.5(–31) cm long, 4–11 cm wide, erect, acute to acuminate, the tip drooping soon after opening, externally greenish white, occasionally flushed with brownish purple towards the margins and along the mid-vein, internally very pale green to almost white, sometimes stained with brownish purple along the margins, entire limb with a translucent quality. *Spadix* 1/4–1/3 as long as the spathe-limb, 4.4–14 cm in total length; appendix clavate, long-stipitate, 3–10 cm long, 4–10 mm wide, pale to dark yellow or dull tawny brown, stipe sometimes pale. *Staminodes* in 2–5 whorls forming a zone 4–10 mm long; bristles filiform, flexuous, 3.5–5 mm long, cream; bases conical, ± verrucate. *Interstices*: upper 1.5–5 mm long, longitudinally ridged, sometimes obscurely so, pale cream, lower 0–3 mm

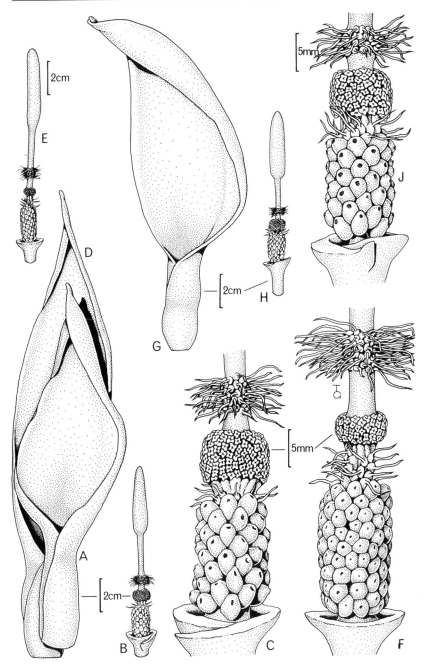

Arum italicum subsp. **italicum**: **A**, spathe; **B**, spadix; **C**, base of spadix. Subsp. **canariense**: **D**, spathe; **E**, spadix; **F**, base of spadix. Subsp. **neglectum**: **G**, spathe; **H**, spadix; **J**, base of spadix.

73

long, with slight longitudinal ridging and some vestigial pistillode bases, cream. *Staminate flowers* in an oblong zone 3–6 mm long, 5–9.5 mm wide; anthers and connectives pale to mid-yellow. *Pistillodes* in 3 or 4 whorls, forming a zone 2.5–3 mm long; bristles filiform, flexuous, 3–5.5 mm long, cream basally, paler apically; bases conic to bulbiform, verrucate to smooth, pale to mid-yellow. *Pistillate flowers* in an oblong-cylindric cluster 9–14 mm long; ovaries ovoid-oblong, 2–3 mm long, pale green to off-white; stigma slightly darker. *Fruiting spike* oblong-cylindric, 5–9(–12) cm long, 2.5–3 cm wide; berries oblong-pyriform, 4–11 mm long, 3.5–5 mm wide. *Germination* epigeal in subsp. *italicum*, hypogeal in subsp. *neglectum*, unknown in subsp. *canariense* and subsp. *albispathum*.

Key to the Subspecies

1. Plant beginning growth in early autumn; leaves all similar in shape, strongly
hastate, posterior lobes widely to moderately divergent, acute   2
Plant beginning growth in early winter; leaves of two distinct types,
winter leaves ovate-hastate, posterior lobes overlapping, obtuse, spring
leaves sagittate-hastate   **c.** subsp. **neglectum**

2. Peduncles and petioles pale to mid-green; spathe-tube interior greenish
white to white, rarely with slight brownish purple staining near the
apex; staminodes in 4 or 5 whorls   3
Peduncles and petioles dull purple; spathe-tube interior purple;
staminodes in 2 or 3 whorls   **b.** subsp. **canariense**

3. Leaves always plain deep green, never marked in any way; spathe almost
white; spadix-appendix pale yellow   **d.** subsp. **albispathum**
Leaves usually with at least some paler veining, often prominently
veined, spotted, blotched or various combinations of these; spathe
pale greenish white to pale yellowish white; spadix-appendix dark
yellow   **a.** subsp. **italicum**

a. subsp. **italicum**

[*A. maculatum* sensu All., Fl. Pedemont. 2: 228 (1785), *non* L. (1763).]

A. maculatum L. var. *italicum* (Miller) Targ.-Tozz. in Inst. Bot. (edn.2)
3: 279 (1813).

A. italicum Miller var. *immaculatum* DC., Fl. Fr. 5: 303 (1815). Type:
not designated.

A. italicum Miller var. *intermedium* Mutel, Fl. Fr. 3: 340 (1836). Type:
not designated.

A. numidicum Schott, Syn. Aroid., 12 (1856). Type: Algeria (holotype

W, destroyed; lectotype selected here: Schott Icones Aroideae no. 1348, W!).

A. ponticum Schott in Bonplandia 10: 148 (1862). Type: Turkey, in ponto, *Kotschy* s.n. (holotype W, destroyed; lectotype selected here: Schott Icones Aroideae no. 1360, W!).

A. divaricatum Dulac, Fl. Haut. Pyr., 46 (1867). Type: not designated.

A. italicum Miller subsp. *gaibolense* Mattei. Place of publication not traced. Type: Italy, Gaibola, presso Bologna, nel'luaghi ambrosi umidi, May 1894, *Mattei* s.n. (holotype FI!).

A. italicum Miller var. *gaibolense* (Mattei) Mattei. Place of publication not traced.

A. modicense Sprenger in Bull. Soc. Tosc. Ortic. 18: 227 (1894). Type: not designated.

A. italicum Miller var. *concolor* Beck v. Mannag., Flora Bosne 2: 59 (1903). Type: Yugoslavia, Dalmatia, *Beck* s.n. (holotype B, destroyed).

A. italicum Miller var. *hercegovinum* Beck v. Mannag., *loc. cit.* Type: Yugoslavia, Mostara, *Pichler* s.n. (holotype PGW).

A. italicum Miller var. *maculatum* Hoschedé in Bull. Acad. Géogr. Bot. 12: 204 (1903). Type: France, Dordogne, *Hoschedé* s.n. (location of type not traced).

A. italicum Miller var. *normale* Briquet, Prodr. Fl. Corse 1: 236 (1910). Type: as for *A. italicum* Miller.

A. italicum Miller var. *yvesii* Briquet, *op. cit.*, 237. Type: Corsica, bord des eaux au Pont du Regino, 20 April 1907, *St. Yves* s.n. (location of type not traced).

A. facchinii Porta ex Hruby in Bull. Soc. Bot. Genève 4: 133 (1912). Type: Italy, in Val Vestino un 800–900 m, *Porta* s.n. (holotype B! isotype FI!).

A. provinciale Somm. ex Hruby, *loc. cit.* Type: Italy, Abbruzzes, (Mt. Cornu, Pouilles) et dans les hautes stations de l'Appenin (location of type not traced).

A. italicum Miller var. *typicum* Engler, Pflanzenr. 73 (IV. 23F): 82 (1920). Type: as for *A. italicum* Miller.

A. italicum Miller var. *typicum* Engler subvar. *immaculatum* (DC.) Engler, *loc. cit.*

A. italicum Miller var. *typicum* Engler subvar. *normale* (Briquet) Engler, *op. cit.*, 83.

A. italicum Miller var. *facchinii* (Porta ex Hruby) Engler, *op. cit.*, 86.

A. majoricense L. Chodat in Bull. Soc. Bot. Genève 15: 194 (1923).

Type: [Majorca] ad sepentrionem urbis Arta, inter culturas opun-
tiarum et simul cum *Aro italico* vigens, *Chodat* s.n. (location of
type not traced).

A. *italicum* Miller var. *typicum* Engler forma *purpurascens* Pamp. in
Nuovo Giorn. Bot. Ital. 35: 302 (1928). Type: Italy, prope
Florentiam, in sepibus inter 'Campo di Marte' et rivum 'Africo',
8 May 1928, *Pampanini* s.n. (holotype FI!).

A. *italicum* Miller subsp. *concinnatum* (Schott) Engler var. *parvulum*
Borhidi in Priszter & Borhidi, *op. cit.*, 162 (1967). Type: Hun-
gary, mons Tubes, prope oppidum Pécs, *Borhidi* 1115 (holotype
UH).

A. *maculatum* L. var. *angustatum* Engler forma *parvulum* (Borhidi)
Terpó in Bot. Közlem. 58: 158 (1971).

A. *italicum* Miller forma *majoricense* (L. Chodat) Mus, Pericás &
Rosselló in Candollea 42: 397 (1987).

A. *italicum* Miller subsp. *euitalicum* Ciferri & Giacomini. Type: Italy,
Vallone di Cala Maesyta, supra il Porto. esp. Sud, 6 May 1966
(FI!). Place of publication not traced, cited in Paoli & Romagnoli
(1976).

[A. *italicum* Miller var. *nigro-maculatum* Fiori *in sched. nom. nud.*]

DESCRIPTION. *Plant* beginning growth in early autumn. *Leaves* all of one
type, strongly hastate, posterior lobes widely divergent, acute, usually with
primary and main lateral veins slightly to heavily silver-grey, cream or
yellowish green, more rarely blade marked with irregular black-purple spots
or cloudy silver-grey blotches, or a combination of any of these, rarely plain
green. *Petiole and peduncle* pale to mid-green. *Spathe-limb* pale greenish white
to pale yellowish white. *Spathe-tube* interior greenish white, rarely stained
purple apically. *Spadix-appendix* dark yellow. *Staminodes* in 4 or 5 whorls, bases
verrucate.

ILLUSTRATIONS. PLATE 2. Phillips & Rix, Bulbs, 153(i) (1989).

FLOWERING PERIOD. Mid-May to mid-June, occasionally extending into
early July.

HABITAT. Open woodland, hedgerows, open scrub, dry pasture, maquis;
sea-level to 1,200 m.

DISTRIBUTION. N Africa (Morocco, Tunisia, Algeria), most of Europe
south of the Netherlands (possibly native in the UK), W and N Turkey, Iraq
(introduced with crops?). Naturalized in Argentina (see Forziano, Crisci &
Delucchi, 1991). MAP 3a, p. 78.

b. subsp. **canariense** (Webb & Berth.) Boyce, **stat. nov.**
A. canariense Webb & Berth., Hist. Nat. Canar. 3(2): 293 (1848);
Schott, Syn. Aroid., 13 (1856) & Prodr. Syst. Aroid., 84 (1860).
Type: Insulae Canaria, Palma, *Webb & Bethelot* s.n. (holotype P!).
A. italicum Miller var. *canariense* (Webb & Berth.) Engler in A. & C.
DC., Monogr. Phan. 2: 592 (1879).

DESCRIPTION. *Plant* beginning growth in early autumn. *Leaves* all of one type, narrowly hastate, basal lobes moderately divergent, deep green. *Petiole and peduncle* dull purple. *Spathe-limb* greenish white, sometimes with slight purple staining basally. *Spathe-tube* interior purple. *Staminodes* in 2 or 3 whorls, bases verrucate.

ILLUSTRATIONS. None traced.

FLOWERING PERIOD. April to May.

HABITAT. Grassy and earthy banks, amongst low scrub, in the shade of large rocks, in clearings in *Laurus* forest; sea-level to 750 m.

DISTRIBUTION. Atlantic Islands (Gran Canaria, Tenerife, Azores, Madeira). MAP 3b, p. 78.

c. subsp. **neglectum** (F. Towns.) Prime in Watsonia 5: 107 (1961).
[? *A. vernale* Salis., Prodr., 261 (1796). Type: not traced.]
A. italicum Miller var. *neglectum* F. Towns., Fl. Hants., 327 (1883).
    Type: England, Isle of Wight, Ventnor, October 1866, *Trimen*
    s.n. (holotype BM!).
A. italicum Miller var. *foucaudii* Corbière, Fl. Norm., 2nd Suppl.
    (1898). Type: France, Dordogne, Manche, Charente inferieure,
    Corbière s.n. (holotype ?P).
A. italicum Miller var. *typicum* Engler subvar. *foucaudii* (Corbière)
    Engler, Pflanzenr. 73 (IV. 23F): 83 (1920).
A. italicum Miller var. *typicum* Engler subvar. *obtusilobum* Hort. ex
    Engler, *loc. cit.* Type: Cult. in Bot. Gard. Berol., 1910 (holotype
    B, destroyed).
A. italicum Miller var. *typicum* Engler subvar. *punctatum* Hort. ex
    Engler, *loc. cit.* Type: Cult. in Bot. Gard. Berol., 1897 (holotype
    B, destroyed).

DESCRIPTION. *Plant* beginning growth in early winter. *Leaves* of two distinct types. Winter leaves ovate-hastate, spring leaves sagittate-hastate, both with short, slightly divergent or overlapping posterior lobes, deep green, rarely with small, jagged purple-black spots. *Petiole and peduncle* brownish purple. *Spathe-limb* pale greenish white with brownish purple staining exter-

78

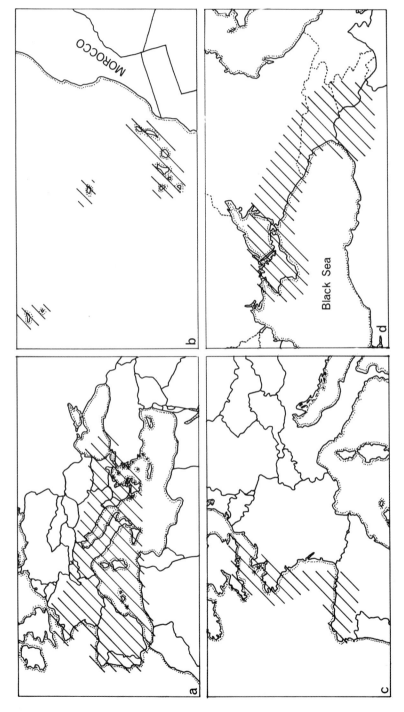

Map 3. Distribution of *Arum italicum*. a: subsp. *italicum*. b: subsp. *canariense*. c: subsp. *neglectum*. d: subsp. *albispathum*.

nally along the margins and mid-vein. *Spathe-tube* often stained internally with brownish purple in the upper half. *Staminodes* in 2 or 3 whorls, bases slightly verrucate.

ILLUSTRATIONS. Phillips, Wild Flowers of Britain, 76(g) (1977).

FLOWERING PERIOD. May to June.

HABITAT. Deciduous woodland margins, hedgerows, occasionally in open pasture (relict from felled woodland?); sea-level to 300 m.

DISTRIBUTION. S England, Channel Islands (Alderney, Guernsey, Jersey), N France, N Spain. MAP 3c, p. 78.

d. subsp. **albispathum** (Steven ex Ledeb.) Prime in Bot. Journ. Linn. Soc. 76: 384 (1978). Prime's attribution of the authorship of *A. albispathum* to Steven is treated here as a bibliographic error.

A. albispathum Steve ex Ledeb., Fl. Ross. 4: 9 (1853); Schott, Syn. Aroid., 10 (1856); Steven in Bull. Soc. Nat. Mosc. 30: 66 (1857). Type: Crimea, Tauria, a Nikita ad Laspi (holotype H).

A. orientale Bieb. var. *albispathum* (Steven ex Ledeb.) Engler in A. & C. DC., Monogr. Phan. 2: 588 (1879). Engler's attribution of the authorship of *A. albispathum* to Steven is treated here as a bibliographic error.

A. orientale Bieb. subsp. *albispathum* (Steven ex Ledeb.) Nyman, Consp. Fl. Europ., 755 (1882).

A. orientale Bieb. subsp. *albispathum* (Steven ex Ledeb.) Richter, Pl. Europ. 1: 172 (1890) *comb. illeg.*

DESCRIPTION. *Plant* beginning growth in early autumn. *Leaves* all of one type, hastate, posterior lobes moderately divergent, acute, plain deep green. *Petiole and peduncle* pale to mid-green. *Spathe-limb* ± white. *Spathe-tube* interior white. *Spadix-appendix* pale yellow. *Staminodes* in 4 or 5 whorls, bases verrucate.

ILLUSTRATIONS. None traced.

FLOWERING PERIOD. Mid-May to mid-June.

HABITAT. Deciduous woodland, banks, scrubby clearings, margins of mixed deciduous and coniferous forest; 100–750 m.

DISTRIBUTION. Crimea, Caucasus. MAP 3d, p. 78.

4. ARUM CONCINNATUM

In 1860 Schott described two species, *A. concinnatum* and *A. nickelii*, which later proved to represent the same taxon. The name *A. nickelii* has been used for some considerable time for the species under discussion here. However, the name *A. concinnatum* has priority since an illustration labelled *A. concinnatum*, and clearly identifiable as such, had already been published by Schott (1859). Although the name *A. nickelii* is far better known to aroid growers than *A. concinnatum*, such potentially unpopular name changes are necessary and indeed important in a genus in which the nomenclature has hitherto been rather chaotic.

Arum concinnatum is an eastern Mediterranean species, common on Crete, but rare on the Turkish mainland. Although a robust plant and, where found, extremely abundant, *A. concinnatum* is rarely collected and is seldom seen in cultivation.

Arum concinnatum has often been confused with *A. byzantinum*, and even recent guides books (Polunin, 1980) have depicted *A. concinnatum* as *A. byzantinum*. In reality the two species are very distinct, and once seen side by side there should be no grounds for confusion. *Arum byzantinum* is a much smaller plant overall, with darker coloured spathes, a shorter, thinner spadix-appendix and generally narrower leaves. In addition, the cloudy, silver leaf markings so distinctive of *A. concinnatum* are entirely absent in *A. byzantinum*.

Although placed in section *Arum* because of its rhizomatous tuber, *A. concinnatum* has no close relatives. On the basis of the massive spadix-appendix and the arrangement of the sterile flowers the closest relative would appear to be *A. rupicola*. However, other features displayed by *A. rupicola*, in particular the discoid tuber and lack of scent (*A. concinnatum* has a very potent urine-like smell in flower), suggest that they are not closely linked.

Arum concinnatum is an easily grown plant with both handsome foliage and attractive spathes. However, for the grower, it has two drawbacks, namely the sheer size of a well-grown plant, and its tender nature. With plenty of moisture the foliage may reach as high as one metre, and thus accommodating such a plant under glass is not easy. The rhizomatous tuber, which travels a considerable distance each season, makes conventional pots unsuitable. A solution to this is to grow *A. concinnatum* in a glasshouse border where it can spread unhindered. Alternatively a large tub can be used. If this is not feasible it is possible to grow *A. concinnatum* out-of-doors in a very sheltered position shaded from early morning sun.

Plate 5

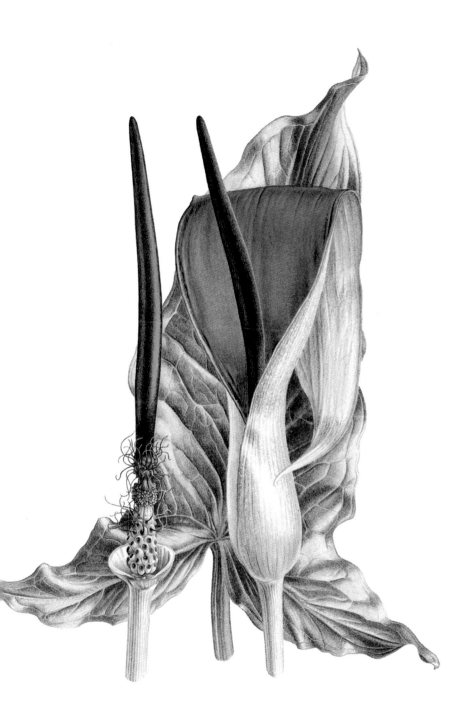

Arum orientale subsp. *sintenisii*   PANDORA SELLARS

Plate 6

Arum cyrenaicum

PANDORA SELLARS

Arum concinnatum Schott, Icones Aroidearum t.39 & 40 (1859) & Prodr. Syst. Aroid., 84 (1860). Type: ex Syra cult. Schönbrunn (holotype W, destroyed; lectotype selected here: Schott Icones Aroideae no. 1259, W!).

A. *byzantinum* Schott in Oesterr. Bot. Wochenbl. 7: 212 (1857), *non* Blume (1836). Type: Crete (holotype W, destroyed; lectotype selected here: Schott Icones Aroideae no. 1245, W!).

A. *marmoratum* Schott, Prodr. Syst. Aroid., 85 (1860). Type: Naxos (holotype W, destroyed; lectotype selected here: Schott Icones Aroideae no. 1335, W!).

A. *nickelii* Schott, *loc. cit.* Type: ex Oriente, *Zelebor* s.n. (holotype W, destroyed; lectotype selected here: Schott Icones Aroideae no. 1342, W!).

A. *italicum* Miller var. *concinnatum* (Schott) Engler in A. & C. DC., Monogr. Phan. 2: 592 (1879).

A. *italicum* Miller var. *byzantinum* (Blume) Engler forma *purpureopetiolatum* Engler, *op. cit.*, 593. ['*purpureopetiolata*']. Type: Crete, Nio Chorio, *Sieber* s.n. (holotype B, destroyed).

A. *italicum* Miller var. *byzantinum* (Blume) Engler forma *viridipetiolatum* Engler, *loc. cit.* ['*viridipetiolata*']. Type: Crete, Nio Chorio, *Sieber* s.n. (holotype B, destroyed).

A. *italicum* Miller subsp. *concinnatum* (Schott) Richter, Pl. Europ. 1: 172 (1890).

A. *wettsteinii* Hruby in Bull. Soc. Bot. Genève 4: 152 (1912). Type: Crete, Canea, in damp places, leaves 6 May 1883, flowers 4 June 1883, *Reverchon* 172 (holotype B, destroyed). Based on one element of *Reverchon* 172; the single sheet of this collection in Berlin has not been annotated by Hruby and so it is assumed here that the holotype has been destroyed.

A. *italicum* Miller var. *concinnatum* (Schott) Engler subvar. *marmoratum* (Schott) Engler, Pflanzenr. 73 (IV. 23F): 85 (1920).

A. *italicum* Miller var. *concinnatum* (Schott) Engler subvar. *nickelii* (Schott) Engler, *loc. cit.*

A. *italicum* Miller var. *concinnatum* (Schott) Engler subvar. *wettsteinii* (Hruby) Engler, *loc. cit.*

A. *italicum* Miller var. *sieberi* Engler, *op. cit.*, 86. Type: Crete, Canea, in damp places, leaves 6 May 1883, flowers 4 June 1883, *Reverchon* 172, (holotype B, destroyed). As in A. *wettsteinii* above, based on one element of *Reverchon* 172; the single sheet of this collection in Berlin has not been annotated by Hruby and it is assumed here that the holotype has been destroyed.

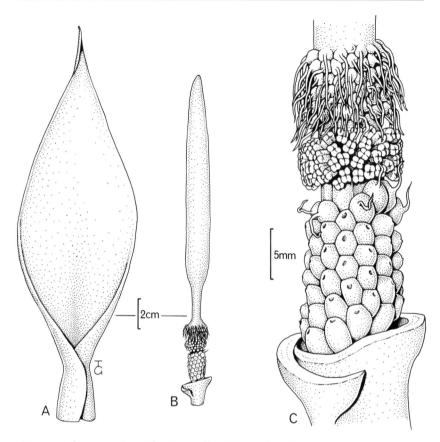

Arum concinnatum. A, spathe; **B**, spadix; **C**, base of spadix.

A. italicum Miller subsp. *concinnatum* (Schott) Engler *apud* Borhidi in
  Priszter & Borhidi, Bot. Közlem. 54: 160 (1967), *comb. illeg.*

DESCRIPTION. *Tuberous herb* sprouting in early autumn from a rhizomatous tuber 7–10 (–15) cm long, 1.5–3.5 cm thick. *Petiole* terete, 20–45 cm long,
5–12 mm wide, dark to mid-green, sometimes flushed with purple basally.
Leaf-blade sagittate-hastate to oblong-sagittate, apex subacute to obtuse, 15–55
cm long, 10–32 cm wide, semi-glossy, dark green, lightly to moderately
blotched with silver-grey above. *Inflorescence* smelling strongly of stale urine.
Peduncle much shorter than the leaves, terete, 5–14 cm long, 7–12 mm wide,
pale to mid-green. *Spathe* 16–29 cm long; spathe-tube oblong-cylindric, 2–5
cm long, 1.5–2.5 cm wide, constricted apically, exterior pale to mid-green,
paler basally, usually flushed with purple along the margin, interior pale

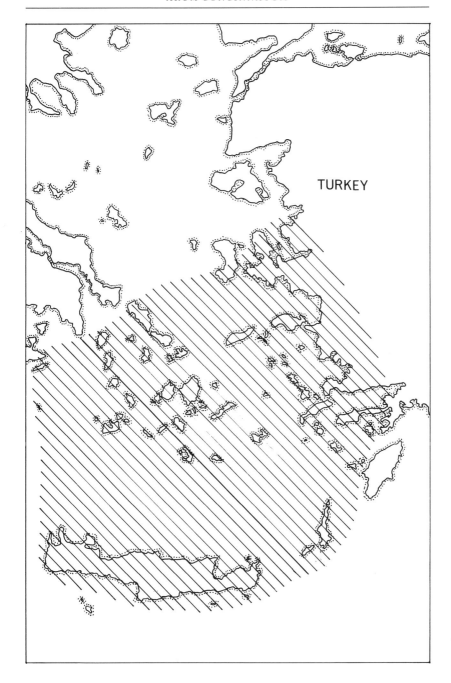

TURKEY

Map 4. Distribution of *Arum concinnatum*.

83

greenish white below, mid-purple above; spathe-limb lanceolate-elliptic to elliptic, 14.5–24 cm long, 7–15 cm wide, erect, apex acuminate, the tip soon drooping after opening, externally pale to mid-green, flushed with pale purple along the margins, especially towards the apex, internally greenish white with scattered shiny, translucent patches, ± flushed with pale purple along the margins and at the apex, rarely the whole spathe pale purple, or entirely pale green. *Spadix* more than ½ as long to just exceeding the spathe-limb, 9–27 cm in total length; appendix massively conic-cylindric to stoutly clavate-cylindric, shortly stipitate, 7–23.5 cm long, 9–15 mm wide, dull ochre-yellow to pale creamy yellow, more rarely pale purplish cream or purple, stipe cream to yellow. *Staminodes* in 5–7 whorls; bristles filiform, flexuous, 6–7 mm long, pale yellow, stained with purple; bases conic, verrucate, pale yellow. *Interstices*: upper 1–2 mm long, longitudinally ridged, pale yellow, lower ± absent. *Staminate flowers* in an oblong zone 5–7 mm long, 9–11 mm wide; anthers and connectives pale yellow, stained with purple apically. *Pistillodes* in *c.* 2 whorls forming a zone 3–5 mm long; bristles filiform, flexuous, 3–4 mm long, pale yellow below, purple above; bases bulbiform, smooth, pale cream. *Pistillate flowers* in a cylindric cluster 9–15 mm long; ovaries ovoid-cylindric, 2.5–3 mm pale green; stigma whitish grey. *Fruiting spike* oblong-pyriform, 6–7 cm long, 2–2.5 cm wide; berries oblong-pyriform, 4–14 mm long, 2.5–5 mm wide. *Germination* epigeal.

ILLUSTRATIONS. PLATE 3. Polunin, Flowers of Greece & the Balkans f.1818 (1980) as *A. italicum* subsp. *byzantinum.*

FLOWERING PERIOD. Late March to early June.

HABITAT. Ditches, wet banks, undisturbed olive groves, often extremely abundant; sea-level to 350 m.

DISTRIBUTION. Greece (extreme southern tip of the Peloponnese), most islands of the E Mediterranean, although apparently absent from Rhodes), coastal SW Turkey. MAP 4, p. 83.

II. Section Dioscoridea

Arum section **Dioscoridea** (Engler) Boyce in Kew Bull. 44: 390 (1989).

['*Arum dioscoridis* group' Hruby in Bull. Soc. Bot. Genève 4: 124, 1912.]

Arum § *Dioscoridea* Engler, Pflanzenr. 72 (IV. 23F): 68 (1920), rankless taxon, see Boyce, 1989). Type: *A. dioscoridis* Sm.

Arum § *Nigra* Engler, *loc. cit.*, rankless taxon, (see Boyce, 1989). Type: *A. nigrum* Schott.

Description as in the key to the sections and subsections (p. 56).

a. Subsection Alpina

Arum subsection **Alpina** Boyce in Kew Bull. 44: 391 (1989). Type: *A. alpinum* Schott & Kotschy.

Peduncles longer than petioles. *Spadix-appendix* clavate, long-stipitate. *Staminodes and pistillodes* with long, filiform, semi-rigid bristles. *Inflorescence* scentless.

5. ARUM ALPINUM

Despite being described over 130 years ago, this quietly attractive species is still almost unknown in cultivation. One reason for this is that for many decades *A. alpinum* has been regarded as being synonymous with *A. maculatum*. Admittedly the two species are superficially similar but, in fact, they differ quite substantially from one another. *Arum alpinum* differs morphologically in the discoid tuber, longer peduncle, different arrangement of the sterile flowers, distinct sculpturing of the staminode and pistillode bases and lack of scent. In addition they possess different chromosome numbers (Terpó, 1973; Bedalov, 1981). *Arum alpinum* also occurs over a wider geographical area than *A. maculatum*, being recorded from southern Spain throughout central, southern and northern Europe and Scandinavia and as far east as Turkey. *Arum alpinum*, as suggested by its wide distribution, is found in a variety of habitats. In northern Europe it is most commonly found in clearings or at the edges of deciduous, or open coniferous, woodland. In Greece and Spain it grows in more open places such as pasture or on grassy slopes among rocks.

Some botanists have proposed a number of varieties and subspecies of *A. alpinum* to represent some of the geographical variation. Many of these names have not been universally accepted, but one of them, subsp. *danicum* (Prime) Terpó, has gained general acceptance. Nielsen & Ugelvig (1986) expressed doubts as to the validity of this separation and my own observations failed to convince me that there are any stable differences between the Scandinavian and European populations of *A. alpinum*. For this reason subsp. *danicum* is not recognized here.

Arum alpinum is gradually becoming better known in cultivation, especially since the introduction of seed from northern Greece and Yugoslavia. It is hoped that similar collections from other localities will eventually become available, especially those from Scandinavia. Compared with the more gaudy species the pale green spathes of *A. alpinum* seem somewhat insignificant. Nevertheless, when seen *en masse* the effect of the spathes in combination with the pale brown to purple spadices is pleasing and this, together with the fact that the species is hardy and easy to grow, make it a worthwhile addition to the garden. As a bonus, the plant fruits very freely, the ripe heads attaining a particularly bright orange-red which rivals that of *A. italicum*.

Arum alpinum Schott & Kotschy in Bot. Zeitung. 9: 285 (1851); Schott, Syn. Aroid., 12 (1856) & Prodr. Syst. Aroid., 91 (1860). Type: Roumania, in alpibus e Transsylvaniae australis in regione *Pini pumilionis* (holotype W, destroyed; lectotype selected here: Schott Icones Aroideae no. 1236, W!). Terpó (1973) selected a lectotype for *A. alpinum*. However the specimen chosen (Hungary, Budapest, in silvaticus montis Janos-Hegy, 19 May 1906, *Filarszky, Kümmerle & Jávorka* 23743/91) is not an element from the protologue and is thus not acceptable as a lectotype.

A. gracile Unverr. in Verh. Mitth. Siebenbürg Vereins Naturwiss. Hermannstadt. 5: 173 (1854). Type: Herbarblatt 3773 (holotype NH).

A. intermedium Schur ex Schott, Prodr. Syst. Aroid., 91 (1860). Type: 'a Schurio mecum communicatum' (holotype W, destroyed; lectotype selected here: Schott Icones Aroideae no. 1276, W!).

A. transsilvanicum Cztez in Erdély. Muz.-Egyl. Evk. 6: 11 (1872). Type: not designated.

A. maculatum L. var. *alpinum* (Schott & Kotschy) Engler in A. & C. DC., Monogr. Phan. 2: 595 (1879).

A. maculatum L. var. *angustatum* Engler, *loc. cit.* Type: based on the types of *A. besserianum* Schott, *A. intermedium* Schur ex Schott; *A. malyi* Schott.

A. maculatum L. subsp. *alpinum* (Schott & Kotschy) Richter, Pl. Europ. 1: 173 (1890).

A. maculatum L. subsp. *angustatum* (Engler) Richter, *loc. cit.*

A. italicum Miller var. *lanceolatum* Boiss. & Heldr. ex Engler, Pflanzenr. 73 (IV. 23F): 86 (1920). Type: Crete, am Amalos, an schattigen Felsen, 1884, *Reverchon* 278 (holotype B! isotypes G! K! L! P!).

A. maculatum L. var. *angustatum* Engler subvar. *alpinum* (Schott & Kotschy) Engler, *op. cit.* 92.

A. maculatum L. var. *angustatum* Engler subvar. *gracile* (Unverr.) Engler, *loc. cit.*

A. maculatum L. var. *attenuatum* Engler, *loc. cit.* Type: Greece, Thessaly, Chaliki, auf Triften, 1896, *Sintenis* 1542 (holotype B, destroyed).

A. maculatum L. subsp. *danicum* Prime in Watsonia 5: 108 (1961). Type: Denmark, Gronnese Skov, nr. Frederiksvoerk, North Zeeland, 11 May 1961, *T.W. Bocher* s.n. (holotype C; isotypes BM! M!).

A. maculatum L. subsp. *alpinum* (Schott & Kotschy) H. Riedl in Phyton 12, 1–4: 166 (1967), *comb. illeg.*

A. alpinum Schott & Kotschy var. *intermedium* (Schur ex Schott) Terpó in Acta Bot. Acad. Sci. Hung. 18(1–2): 235 (1973).

A. alpinum Schott & Kotschy var. *pannonicum* Terpó, *loc. cit.* Type: Hungary, Eupannonicum, Mosonmagyaróvár, auf der Leitha (Lajta), 1969, *Czimber, Erdös & Terpó* 14475 (holotype KEH).

A. alpinum Schott & Kotschy var. *pannonicum* Terpó forma *javorkae* Terpó, *loc. cit.* Type: Hungary, Bakonyikum orient., Csatka-Koromlapsz, 1969, *Terpó-Pomogyi, Terpó & Link* 14471 (holotype KEH).

A. alpinum Schott & Kotschy subsp. *danicum* (Prime) Terpó, *op. cit.*, 238.

A. alpinum Schott & Kotschy subsp. *gracile* (Unverr.) Terpó, *loc. cit.*

A. orientale Bieb. subsp. *danicum* (Prime) Prime, *nom. nud.*? Stated in *Flora Europaea* 5: 270 (1980) to have been published in *J. Linn. Soc., Bot.* 76: 384 (1978). The validation does not appear there and I have been unable to trace another place of publication.

DESCRIPTION. *Tuberous herb* sprouting in early winter from a discoid, vertically orientated tuber 3–5 cm across, 1.5–2 cm thick. *Petiole* terete, 12–18 (–23) cm long, 3–4 mm wide, dark green to mid-green, the lower ¼ occasionally stained with purple. *Leaf-blade* sagittate to sagittate-hastate, apex acute to obtuse, 9–13 cm long, 3–7.5 cm wide, mid-green. *Inflorescence* unscented. *Peduncle* equal to or exceeding the leaves, terete, 11–18 cm long, 4–5 mm wide, light green to mid-green, the lower ⅓ occasionally stained with purple. *Spathe* 9–14 cm long; spathe-tube oblong-cylindric, 2–3 cm long, 1.5–1.75 cm wide, moderately constricted apically, exterior pale green, interior with the basal ⅓ very pale greenish white, upper ⅔ purple; spathe-limb elliptic-lanceolate, 7–9 cm long, 3.5–4.5 cm wide, erect, acumin-

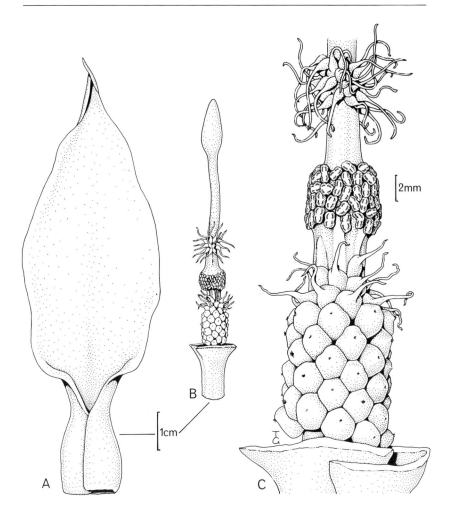

Arum alpinum. **A**, spathe; **B**, spadix; **C**, base of spadix.

ate, externally and internally pale green. *Spadix* ⅓–⅔ as long as the spathe-limb, 5–8 cm in total length; appendix slender-cylindric, slightly to moderately clavate, long-stipitate, 3–5 cm long, 2.5–4 mm wide, pale chocolate-brown to dull purple, stipe fading to cream basally. *Staminodes* in 2 or 3 whorls forming a zone 2–4 mm long; bristles filiform, semi-rigid, 5–6 mm long, cream; bases bulbiform, verrucate, dull yellow. *Interstices*: upper 3–5 mm long, smooth, primrose-yellow; lower 2–3 mm long, lower portion with rudimentary pistillode bases, off-white. *Staminate flowers* in a cylindric zone 5–6 mm long, 3–4 mm wide; anthers purple and connectives yellow. *Pistillodes* in 3–5 whorls forming a zone 3–5 mm long; bristles aristate-filiform,

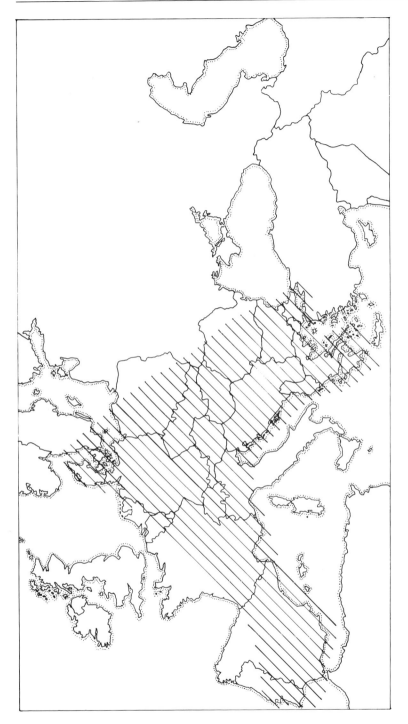

Map 5. Distribution of *Arum alpinum*.

semi-rigid, 3–4 mm long, cream; bases elongate-bulbiform, slightly verrucate, pale yellow. *Pistillate flowers* in an oblong-cylindric cluster 15–20 mm long; ovaries oblong, tapering apically, 2–3 mm long, pale greenish yellow, darker towards the stigma; stigma dirty white. *Fruiting spike* oblong-cylindric, 4–5 cm long, 1.5–2 cm wide; berries pyriform, 5–9 mm long, 3–5 mm wide. *Germination* hypogeal.

ILLUSTRATIONS. PLATE 4. Acta Bot. Acad. Sci. Hung. 18(1–2): 233, t.11 (1973); Bull. Alpine Gard. Soc. 54: 38 (1986) as *A. maculatum*.

FLOWERING PERIOD. Late May to mid-June, occasionally into late June.

HABITAT. Deciduous woodland, edges of coniferous woodland, open grassy slopes, pasture, rocky slopes; 450–1,700 m.

DISTRIBUTION. Throughout Europe from southern Spain to the Balkans, and from southern Sweden to Crete, NW Turkey. MAP 5, p. 89.

b. Subsection Dischroochiton

Arum subsection **Discroochiton** Schott, Prodr. Syst. Aroid., 75 (1860). Lectotype: *A. orientale* Bieb. (selected by Boyce in Kew Bull. 44: 391, 1989).

Peduncles shorter than petioles. *Spadix-appendix* long-stipitate, usually stout. *Pistillodes* very well developed, with long, filiform, flexuous bristles. *Staminodes* either similar or with stiff, aristate bristles. *Inflorescence* foetid, sweet-oily or smelling of fermenting fruit.

6. ARUM ORIENTALE

Arum orientale is a common species in the wild, but surprisingly, has never become common in cultivation, despite its undoubted hardiness. Originally collected by Marschall von Bieberstein from the Crimea or Caucasus, the species extends from there westwards through northern and western Turkey and into eastern Europe as far west as Vienna. In the south *A. orientale* is represented in Cyprus by subsp. *sintenisii*. Throughout its range *A. orientale* is found in open woodland and in damp shady places. Many of the more northerly sites are subject to cold and wet winter conditions and for this reason *A. orientale* makes an excellent garden subject in the British Isles.

Superficially *A. orientale* resembles *A. maculatum*, and often occurs in similar habitats. However, the two are not closely related, displaying different tuber types, inflorescence scents, spathe coloration and growth regimes. The wide distribution of *A. orientale* is accompanied by much variation in its appearance, and some of these variations have been given formal rank. I have looked carefully at these variants and find that in some cases they do not merit recognition. The exceptions are *A. orientale* subsp. *longispathum* described from Yugoslavia and *A. orientale* subsp. *sintenisii* based on material from northern Cyprus. These taxa display a number of features that justify the subspecific rank adopted here.

Arum longispathum was described by Reichenbach (1845) based on a plant from Yugoslavia, but I have seen very little material of this species; there is only a single specimen at Kew. Bedalov (1981) has carried out exhaustive cytological research into this plant, which she called *A. orientale* subsp. *longispathum*, the name accepted here. The illustration that accompanies the protologue depicts a most distinctive plant, which is none the less closely related to *A. orientale*.

The name *sintenisii* was proposed by Engler in *Das Pflanzenreich* (1920) as *A. orientale* subsp. *elongatum* var. *sintenisii* for material collected in northern Cyprus by Sintenis and Rigo. It differs from typical *A. orientale* by the overall larger size, the longer peduncle, smaller, relatively narrower spathe, stalkless spadix-appendix and sweet, fermenting inflorescence odour. Engler's placing of *sintenisii* into *A. elongatum* is not acceptable, the Cypriot plant is clearly different from *A. elongatum*, differing in the longer peduncle, paler spathe, less massive spadix-appendix and less foetid inflorescence. The similarity of these Cyprus collections to *A. orientale* is unmistakable, however, with the pale purple-washed spathe-limb and slender spadix-appendix all indicating a close link. Nevertheless the morphological distinctions outlined above, together with the geographical disjunction from the main populations of *A. orientale*, support the rank of subspecies proposed here, giving the combination *A. orientale* subsp. *sintenisii*.

Arum orientale subsp. *amoenum*, described from material gathered by Sintenis near Trabzon in north-eastern Turkey is referable to *A. maculatum*.

Arum orientale is a member of a group of species mostly confined to the eastern Mediterranean. The group is distinguished by purple to mauve spathes, a rather slender, usually stipitate spadix-appendix, numerous slender sterile flowers and a moderately strong, dung-like smell when in flower. The closest relative of *A. orientale* appears to be either *A. cyrenaicum* or *A. purpureospathum*. The status of many eastern European populations of *A. orientale* has yet to be finalized. A start has been made (e.g. Dihoru, 1970a; 1970b) but much remains to be done.

Arum orientale Bieb., Fl. Taur.-Cauc. 2: 407 (1808); Schott, Syn. Aroid., 15 (1856) & Prodr. Syst. Aroid., 88 (1860); Engler in A. & C. DC., Monogr. Phan. 2: 586 (1879); Hruby in Bull. Soc. Bot. Genève 4: 140 (1912); Engler, Pflanzenr. 73 (IV. 23F): 78 (1920); Mayo & Meikle in Meikle, Fl. Cyprus 2: 1667 (1985). Type: Crimea or Caucasus, frequens in umbrosis sylvaticis tam Tauriae, quam Caucasi, *Marschall von Bieberstein* s.n. (syntypes LE!).

DESCRIPTION. *Tuberous herb* sprouting in mid-autumn to late autumn from a discoid, horizontally orientated tuber 4–6 cm across, 2–2.5 cm thick. *Petiole terete*, 18–46 cm long, 3–7 mm wide, deep green, usually stained with purple, especially towards the base. *Leaf-blade* broadly hastate, apex obtuse to subacute, 8.5–25 cm long, 5.5–17 cm wide, deep green. *Inflorescence* smelling moderately of horse-dung (subsp. *orientale*, subsp. *longispathum*) or sweet, fermeting (subsp. *sintenisii*). *Peduncle* much shorter than to almost equalling the leaves, terete, 11–19 cm long, 3–4 mm wide, deep green, sometimes stained with purple. *Spathe* 14.5–30 cm long; spathe-tube oblong-cylindric, 2.5–5.5 cm long, 1.5–2.5 cm wide, constricted apically, exterior mid-green with dull purple staining towards the margin and apex, fading to greenish white at the base, interior greenish white below, purple above; spathe-limb ovate to ovate-lanceolate, 12–24.5 cm long, 4–7 cm wide, erect at first but the apex soon flopping forwards, acute to rather bluntly acute, externally pale to mid-green, heavily to moderately stained purple, median vein pale green, internally similarly coloured, but with much heavier purple staining, apex mid-green. *Spadix* ⅓–½ as long as the spathe-limb, 5.5–16 cm in total length; appendix slender-clavate to cylindric, long-stipitate or stalkless, 3.5–13 cm long, 3.6–6.5 cm wide, dull mid-purple, stipe when present generally paler. *Staminodes* in *c.* 2 whorls forming a zone 4–7.5 mm long, yellow, flushed with purple; bases conic, ± smooth, yellow. *Interstices*: upper 2.5–4 mm long, sparsely grooved, minutely verrucate, yellow; lower ± absent. *Staminate flowers* in an quadrate zone 2–5.5 mm long, 3–5 mm wide; anthers yellow with purple tips, connectives yellow. *Pistillodes* in 3 or 4 whorls forming a zone 3–7 mm long; bristles filiform, flexuous, 2.5–6 mm long, yellow, flushed with purple; bases compressed conic, smooth, deep yellow. *Pistillate flowers* in a globose-cylindric cluster, 4.5–20 mm long; ovaries globose, 1.5–2 mm long, dull oblive-green, stained with purple apically; stigma papillose, green. *Fruiting head* cylindric, 4–5.6 cm long, 2–2.5 cm wide; berries oblong, 5–10 mm long, 3.5–5 mm wide. *Germination* epigeal in subsp. *sintenisii*, unknown in subsp. *orientale* and subsp. *longispathum*.

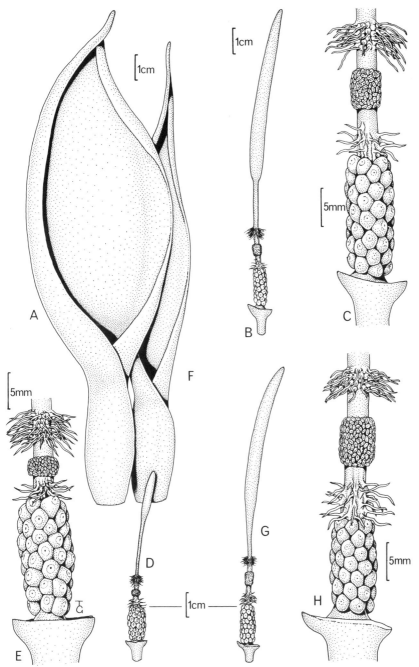

Arum orientale subsp. **orientale**: **A**, spathe; **B**, spadix; **C**, base of spadix; **D**, spadix (to show variation); **E**, base of spadix (to show variation). Subsp. **longispathum**: **F**, spathe; **G**, spadix; **H**, base of spadix.

Key to the Subspecies

1. Spathe-limb elliptic-ovate, acute; spadix-appendix cylindric   2
   Spathe-limb linear-lanceolate, acuminate; spadix-appendix clavate
   c. subsp. **longispathum**

2. Peduncle much shorter than the petioles; spadix-appendix stipitate
   a. subsp. **orientale**
   Peduncle as long as the petioles; spadix-appendix stalkless
   b. subsp. **sintenisii**

a. subsp. **orientale**

A. maculatum L. var. *caucasicum* Willd., Sp. Pl., (edn.4), 483 (1805). Type: not designated.

A. petteri Schott, Syn. Aroid., 12 (1856). Type Dalmatia, *Petter* s.n. (holotype W, destroyed; lectotype selected here: Schott Icones Aroideae no. 1408, W!).

A. consobrinum Schott, Prodr. Syst. Aroid., 87 (1860). Type: Caucasus (holotype LE).

A. incomptum Schott, *op. cit.*, 88, *pro parte, incl. type.* Type: Turkey, Erzurum, Mons Zorab (holotype K!).

A. orientale Bieb. var. *petteri* (Schott) Engler in A. & C. DC., Monogr. Phan. 2: 587 (1879).

A. orientale Bieb. subsp. *petteri* (Schott) Nyman, Consp. Fl. Europ., 754 (1882).

A. orientale Bieb. subsp. *petteri* (Schott) Richter, Pl. Europ. 1: 172 (1890), *comb. illeg.*

A. orientale Bieb. var. *typicum* Zelentzky, Prodr. Fl. Taur., 324 (1906). Type as for *A. orientale* Bieb.

A. nigrum Schott var. *petteri* (Schott) Engler, Pflanzenr. 73 (IV. 23F): 75 (1920).

A. orientale Bieb. subsp. *euorientale* Engler, *op. cit.*, 78. Type: as for *A. orientale* Bieb.

?*A. orientale* Bieb. subsp. *euorientale* Engler var. *albescens* Engler, *loc. cit.* Type. Iran, bei Assalim (holotype W, destroyed).

[*A. pictum* sensu Petter in Bot. Wegw. Nr. 114 (1852), *non* L. fil. (1782).]

DESCRIPTION. As in key.
ILLUSTRATIONS. None traced.
FLOWERING PERIOD. May to June.

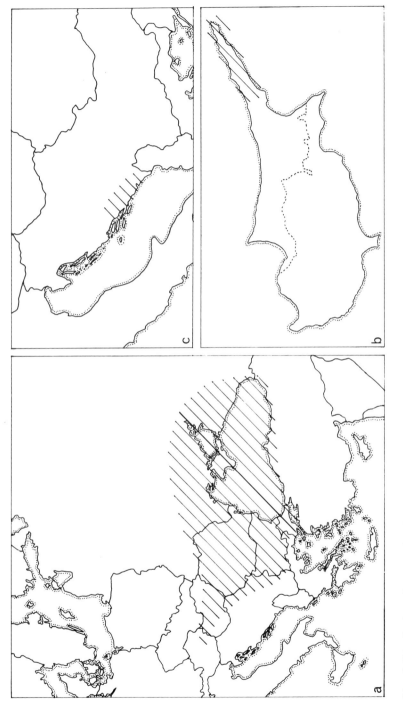

Map 6. Distribution of *Arum orientale*. a: subsp. *orientale*. b: subsp. *sintenisii*. c: subsp. *longispathum*.

HABITAT. Deciduous woodland, on the margins of coniferous woodland, scrubby hillsides amongst rocks, banks; sea-level to 950 m.

DISTRIBUTION. From Austria (area around Vienna) and Poland to NE Turkey, the Crimea and Caucasus. MAP 6a, p. 95.

b. subsp. **sintenisii** (Engler) Boyce, **stat. nov.**

A. orientale Bieb. subsp. *elongatum* var. *sintenisii* Engler, Pflanzenr. 73 (IV. 23F): 80 (1920). Type: Cyprus, auf Triften bei Kythraea, 6 May 1880, *Sintenis & Rigo* 130 (holotype K!).

DESCRIPTION. As in key.
ILLUSTRATION. PLATE 5. No others traced.
FLOWERING PERIOD. April to May.
HABITAT. Uncultivated olive groves; 50–200 m.
DISTRIBUTION. Northern Cyprus (Kythraea). MAP 6b, p. 95.

An attractive and easily grown plant that appears to be more heat-tolerant than the typical subspecies. Its hardiness is as yet not fully tested, although it has passed unscathed through two relatively mild winters in Surrey.

c. subsp. **longispathum** (Reichb.) Engler in Engler, Pflanzenr. 73 (IV. 23F): 80 (1920).

A. longispathum Reichb., Ic. Fl. Germ. 7: 5, t.19 (1845); Schott, Syn. Aroid., 13 (1856) & Prodr. Syst. Aroid., 96 (1860). Type: Yugoslavia, crescit in Dalmatia, Ginegro Stielo, May, *F. August* s.n. (holotype B, destroyed).

DESCRIPTION. As in key.
ILLUSTRATIONS. Apart from the illustration accompanying the protologue (Reichenbach, 1845) I have been unable to trace any illustrations of this plant.
FLOWERING PERIOD. May to June.
HABITAT. Deciduous woodland, in soil pockets amongst rocks; 50–700 m.
DISTRIBUTION. Yugoslavia (Dalmatian Mountains). MAP 6c, p. 95.

Subsp. *longispathum* is a distinctive plant that is at present not in cultivation. The narrow, tapering spathe-limb and the short spadix-appendix make it easily recognizable. For many years after its discovery, subsp. *longispathum* was known only from the type collection. A few specimens appear to have been collected by Maly, but most of these were destroyed during the Second World War. A single

Plate 7

Arum purpureospathum $\times$ 2/3

PANDORA SELLARS

Plate 8

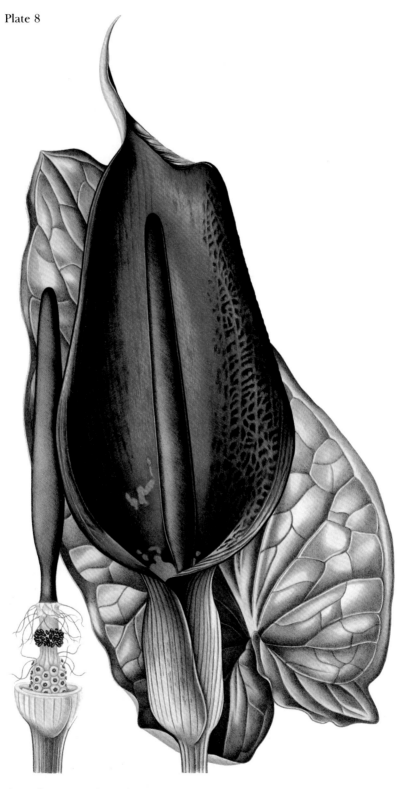

Arum elongatum subsp. *elongatum*

ANN FARRER

specimen at Kew is annotated 'Ex. Herb Schott' and is presumably one of the Maly collections. In recent years living material of subsp. *longispathum* has been recollected on several occasions, although, apparently, only in and around the original locality.

7. ARUM GRATUM

In a genus which is notorious for producing strong odours it is a pleasant change to encounter a species that smells agreeable. *Arum gratum*, a relative of *A. orientale* and included within that widespread taxon by some authors, is such a species. Collected in the Lebanon over a century ago, *A. gratum* was unknown in cultivation until the 1980s when it was recollected in north-western Turkey by Norman Stevens. When I was first shown living material of this collection I was unable to identify it and for a considerable time was sure that the plants represented an undescribed species. I even suggested a name for it, *A. stevensii*. It was not until much later that specimens of *A. gratum* from the Lebanon were compared with the Turkish collections, and were found to represent the same species.

Arum gratum shares with its nearest ally, *A. orientale* subsp. *orientale*, a pale purple-washed spathe-limb, a cryptic inflorescence and a bicoloured spathe-tube interior. It differs from subsp. *orientale* by having the inflorescence borne at ground level, a shorter, broader, almost sessile spathe, shorter spadix-appendix, sweet, not foetid odour at anthesis and much smaller habit.

As well as being an interesting species from a taxonomic standpoint, *A. gratum* is a worthwhile horticultural subject. It is a small plant, easily accommodated in an 18 cm pot. The deep green, glossy leaves just conceal the delicately purple-washed spathe which is borne at ground level, very often with the base of the spathe-tube partially buried. In addition to the attractive spathe colour, a scent reminiscent of crushed SMOKE-BUSH leaves (*Cotinus coggygria*) is noticeable for most of the time that the spathe is open. The main collection of *A. gratum* in cultivation in the UK at present originates from Abant Bölü in north-western Turkey, and has proved to be perfectly hardy. Even so, its small stature means that it is liable to be swamped in the open garden by other more vigorous plants. For this reason, and because it is easier to appreciate the delicate perfume when in flower, I would recommend pot or frame culture.

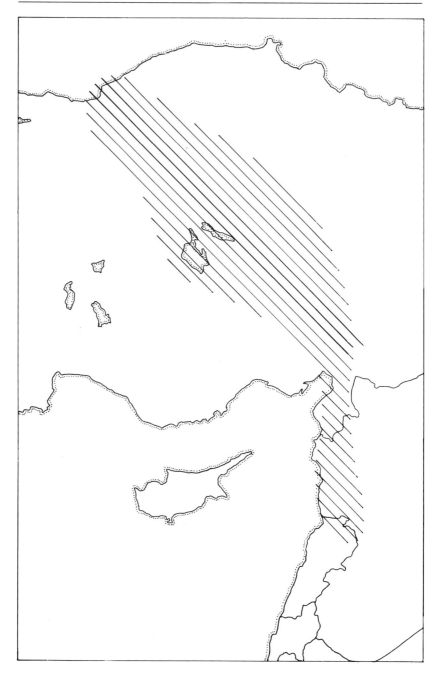

Map 7. Distribution of *Arum gratum*.

More recent collections made by Mathew in southern Turkey and by Drummond from the Bölü area have included larger, more vigorous clones and material with purple-black blotched leaves and spathes.

Arum gratum Schott, Syn. Aroid., 11 (1856) & Prodr. Syst. Aroid., 89 (1860). Type: Lebanon, in Libani ad Becherne et circa cedretum, 21 July 1855, *Kotschy* s.n. (holotype W, destroyed; isotypes BM! G! P!).
A. orientale Bieb. var. *gratum* (Schott) Engler in A. & C. DC., Monogr.
  Phan. 2: 588 (1879) & in Engler, Pflanzenr. 73 (IV. 23F): 79 (1920).
[*A. stevensii* Boyce, *nom. nud.*]

DESCRIPTION. *Tuberous herb* sprouting in early winter from a discoid, vertical tuber 3.4–5 cm across, 1.5–2.5 cm thick. *Petiole terete*, 17.5–25 (–30) cm long (up to 50 cm long according to Mouterde, 1966), 3–4.5 mm wide, deep green. *Leaf-blade* hastate-sagittate to oblong-hastate, apex subacute, 9–18 cm long, 7–12 cm wide, deep green, occasionally with jagged purple-black blotches. *Inflorescence* sweet-smelling. *Peduncle* very much shorter than the leaves, often absent above soil level, 0–2.5 cm long, 4–5 mm wide, pale green, longitudinally striped with reddish brown. *Spathe* 12–18.5 cm long; spathe-tube often partially buried, oblong-ventricose, 2–3.5 cm long, 1.5–2 cm wide, constricted apically, exterior off-white below (if buried) or pale green (if exposed), mid-green, stained with purple above, this colour intensifying towards the margins and apex, interior with a pale greenish white lower half and purple upper half; spathe-limb elliptic-ovate, 10–15 cm long, 5–6.5 cm wide, cucullate, acute to minutely acuminate, externally pale green flushed with pale purple, apex and median vein greenish, internally olive-green, ± flushed with pale purple, occasionally with jagged purple-black blotches. *Spadix* less than ⅓ as long as the spathe-limb, 5.5–6.5 cm in total length; appendix strongly clavate, stipitate, 4–4.5 cm long, 5–6 mm wide, reddish purple to greenish purple, stipe purple. *Staminodes* in *c.* 3 whorls forming a zone 1.5–2 mm long; bristles filiform, flexuous, 2.5–3.5 mm long, cream, tipped with purple; bases conic, smooth, cream. *Interstices*: upper 0.5–1 mm long, smooth, cream; lower ± absent. *Staminate flowers* in an oblong zone 4–5 mm long, 3.5–4 mm wide; anthers and connectives dull purple. *Pistillodes* in 1 whorl forming a zone 0.5–1 mm long; bristles aristate, stiff, 1.5–2 mm long, cream, minutely tipped with purple; bases globose, smooth, pale cream. *Pistillate flowers* in a globose-cylindric cluster 5–7 mm long; ovaries globose, 1.5–2 mm long, cream, barely stained with purple apically; stigma white. *Fruiting spike* cylindric, 3–4.5 cm long, 2–2.5 cm wide; berries pyriform, 7–10 mm long, 3.5–4.5 mm wide. *Germination* unknown.

99

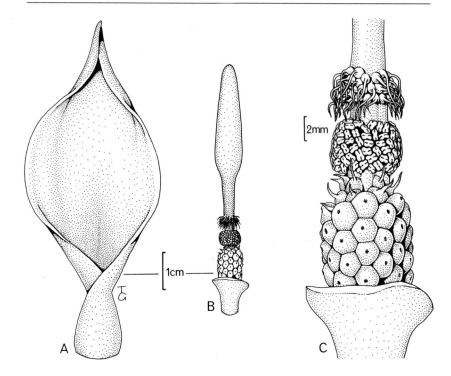

Arum gratum. **A**, spathe; **B**, spadix; **C**, base of spadix.

ILLUSTRATIONS. None traced.
FLOWERING PERIOD. May to June, rarely into July.
HABITAT. Garigue, *Cedrus* woodland, deciduous woodland; 550–1,500 m.
DISTRIBUTION. Syria, Lebanon, W Turkey. MAP 7, p. 89.

8. ARUM LUCANUM

Although described by Cavara & Grande over 80 years ago this species is seldom seen in herbaria and has only recently been introduced into cultivation. *Arum lucanum* is a native of southern Italy, where it is apparently restricted to mountainous regions. There has been some controversy as to whether *A. lucanum* is the correct name for this species since there is an earlier name, *A. cylindraceum*, published by Gasparrini (1844), that has been regarded as possibly referable to *A. lucanum*. Pignatti (1982) held the view that *A. cylindraceum* was an imperfectly known species, but stated that Bedalov

100

regarded that *A. cylindraceum* and *A. lucanum* or *A. alpinum* might be conspecific. Later Bedalov (1984) referred to *A. cylindraceum* as a synonym of *A. alpinum*. If this were to be upheld, however, the correct name for the species would be *A. cylindraceum*, since *A. cylindraceum* (1844) predates *A. alpinum* (1851).

Beauret (1977) stated that he believed that *A. cylindraceum* was related to, rather than referable to, *A. alpinum*. This idea is similar to the approach of Engler (1920) who placed *A. cylindraceum* as a subvariety of *A. maculatum*.

With such a clouded nomenclatural history it was with some surprise that I read the protologue of *A. cylindraceum* since it clearly states that the leaves and spathe of the plant had black to purple spots, a character typical of *A. maculatum*. However, when I saw that type material, eventually traced to Florence by Dr Charles Jarvis, it appeared that *A. cylindraceum* was more similar to *A. alpinum* than *A. maculatum*. For the time being I prefer to follow Pignatti (1982) and regard *A. cylindraceum* as a *species dubiae*.

Prime (1978) published *A. lucanum* as a subspecies of *A. orientale*. Unfortunately Prime's article lacked any discussion as to why he followed this course of action.

Arum lucanum Cavara & Grande in Bull. Orto Bot. Regia Univ. Napoli 3: 409 (1911); Pignatti, Flora d'Italia, 626 (1982). Type: Italy, Lago di Zapano, 1380 m, *Cavara & Grande* s.n. (holotype NAP!).
A. orientale Bieb. subsp. *lucanum* (Cavara & Grande) Prime in Bot. Journ. Linn. Soc. 76: 384 (1978).

DESCRIPTION. *Tuberous herb* sprouting in autumn from a discoid, vertically orientated tuber 3–4 cm across, 2–2.5 cm thick. *Petiole* terete, 6–12 cm long, 3–4 mm wide, deep green. *Leaf-blade* ovate-cordate, apex acute, 6–12 cm long, 4–5 cm wide, deep green. *Inflorescence* smelling weakly of dung. *Peduncle* shorter than the leaves, 10–12 cm long, 4–5 mm wide, deep green. *Spathe* 8.5–13 cm long; spathe-tube cylindric, 2.5–3 cm long, *c.* 1 cm wide, barely constricted apically, exterior pale green, interior greenish white; spathe-limb lanceolate-oblong, acuminate, erect, 6–10 cm long, 2–3 cm wide, externally pale greenish yellow, internally similarly coloured but with faint purplish red staining, especially along the margins. *Spadix c.* ¾ as long as the spathe-limb, 4–5 cm in total length; appendix slender-cylindric, tapering slightly towards the base, 2–2.5 cm long, 2–3 mm wide, dark purple. *Staminodes* in 5 or 6 whorls forming a zone 3–4 mm long; bristles filiform, flexuous, 3–6 mm long, cream tipped with purple; bases globose, verruculose, cream. *Interstices:*

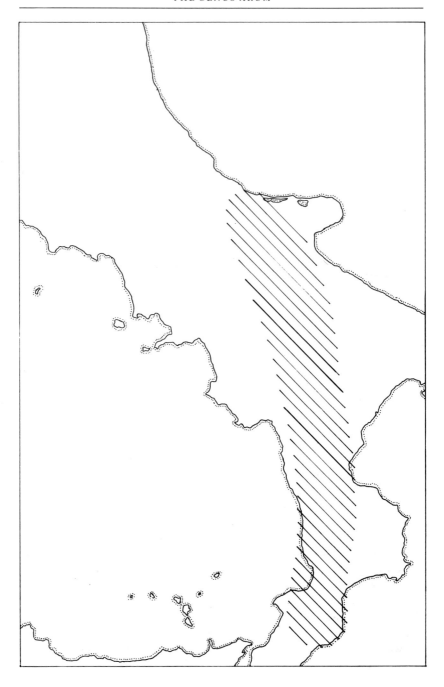

Map 8. Distribution of *Arum lucanum*.

upper ± absent, lower *c.* 1.5–2 mm long, cream. *Staminate flowers* in a subquadratic zone 2–3 mm long, 3–4 mm wide, purple. *Pistillodes* in 2 or 3 whorls forming a zone 1–2 mm long; bristles filiform, flexuous, 4–8 mm long, cream, tipped with purple; bases globose, verruculose, cream. *Pistillate flowers* in a globose cluster 4–14 mm long, 3.5–5 mm wide; ovary oblong-cylindric to globose-oblong, 2–3.5 mm long, pale green, stigma darker. *Fruiting spike* unknown. *Germination* unknown.

ILLUSTRATIONS. None traced.

FLOWERING PERIOD. April to May.

HABITAT. Garrigue; 1,300–1,700 m.

DISTRIBUTION. S. Italy, mountains (Monte dei Fiori, Marsica, Matese, Basil, Monte Papa, Pollino). MAP 8, p. 102.

9. ARUM APULUM

Arum apulum is an attractive but little-known species from southern Italy that serves as a good example of how cytology can help to untangle complicated taxonomic relationships. Carano first published this taxon as a variety of *A. nigrum* in 1934 to account for the supposed Italian populations of an otherwise Balkan species. However, *A. apulum* and *A. nigrum* are not especially closely related. The filiform staminodes and pistillodes, slender spadix-appendix and pale purple and green spathe-limb suggest that *A. apulum* is related to *A. orientale* rather than to *A. nigrum*, and it is puzzling that Carano did not recognize these similarities and combine it with *A. orientale* rather than *A. nigrum*. Moreover, the obvious dissimilarities between *A. apulum* and *A. nigrum* have been reinforced by the cytological work of Gori (1958) and Bedalov (1973, 1975b, 1980). These cytological findings, combined with the morphological and geographical differences, support the proposal of Bedalov (1980) that *A. apulum* deserves specific status. However, although Pignatti (1982) and Bedalov (1984) both refer to '*A. apulum* (Carano) Bedalov' it does not yet seem to have been validly published.

Arum apulum is related to *A. orientale* and *A. nigrum* on the basis of having a slender, stipitate spadix-appendix, foetid, purple inflorescence and a bicoloured purple-and-white spathe-tube interior. Comparison of *A. apulum* with *A. orientale* reveals that the unstained ovary apices, spathe with a high proportion of green along the margins and apex and the more southerly distribution of *A. apulum* easily distinguish them. The differences between *A. apulum* and *A. nigrum* include the former's slender, far more numerous sterile flowers, much more slender spadix-appendix and paler spathe-limb colour.

Arum apulum has recently been introduced into cultivation and, to date, has proven to be an easily cultivated and attractive plant.

Arum apulum (Carano) Boyce, stat. nov.

A. nigrum Schott var. *apulum* Carano in Ann. Bot. 20(3): 584, t.17 (1934). Type: Italy, Bari, Gioia de Colle (holotype FI! isotype NAP).

[*A. apulum* (Carano) Bedalov in Bot. Helvet. 94: 385 (1984), *comb. ined.*]

DESCRIPTION. *Tuberous herb* sprouting in late autumn from a discoid, vertically orientated tuber 4–6 cm across, 2–2.5 cm thick. *Petiole* terete, 12–34 cm long, 2–4.5 mm wide, dull green, stained with purple for *c.* ¼ of its length. *Leaf-blade* hastate-sagittate, apex subacute, 8–16 cm long, 5–13 cm wide, deep green. *Inflorescence* smelling very weakly of horse-dung and urine. *Peduncle* much shorter than the leaves, terete, 4–11 cm long, 3–5 mm wide, dull purple. *Spathe* 12–18 cm long; spathe-tube oblong-ellipsoid, 4–4.5 cm long, 1.5–2 cm wide, constricted apically, exterior mid-green, interior purple, paler towards the apex; spathe-limb oblong-lanceolate, 7–10.5 cm long, 3–5 cm wide, erect, acuminate, externally purplish green, green towards the margin, internally dark purple, the margin and apex mid-green. *Spadix c.* ⅓ as long as the spathe-limb, 4–6 cm in total length; appendix slender-clavate, long-stipitate, 3–4 cm long, 3–5 mm wide, purple, stipe reddish purple. *Staminodes* in 3 or 4 whorls, forming a zone 3–4 mm long; bristles filiform, flexuous, 3–3.5 mm long, purplish cream; bases compressed-conic, verrucate, cream. *Interstices*: upper 3.5–4 mm long, longitudinally ridged, cream; lower 2–3 mm long, ± smooth, cream. *Staminate flowers* in an oblong zone 2.5–3 mm long, 5–5.5 mm wide; anthers purple and connectives cream. *Pistillodes* in 1 or 2 whorls forming a zone 1.5–2 mm long; bristles filiform, flexuous, 3–7 mm long, purplish cream; bases bulbiform, verrucate, cream. *Pistillate flowers* in an oblong-cylindric cluster 7–11 mm long, 5–7 mm wide; ovaries oblong, truncate apically, 2.5–3.5 mm long, pale lime-green; stigma purple. *Fruiting spike* oblong-cylindric, 3–5 cm long, 2–2.5 cm wide; berries oblong-pyriform, 5–9 mm long, 4–6 mm wide. *Germination* unknown.

ILLUSTRATION. Apart from the plate accompanying the protologue (Carano, 1934) I have been unable to trace an illustration.

FLOWERING PERIOD. April.

HABITAT. Low scrub on terra-rossa; 300–400 m.

DISTRIBUTION. S Italy (Puglia, known only from Gioia del Colle). MAP 9, p. 105.

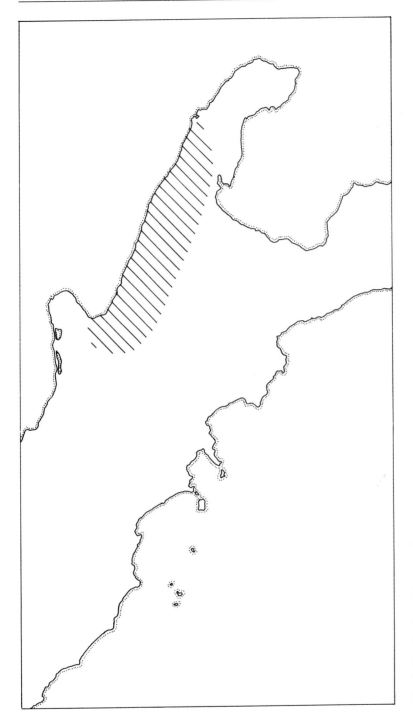

Map 9. Distribution of *Arum apulum*.

10. ARUM NIGRUM

Originating from the Balkans, *A. nigrum* is a glorious species that deserves to be better known. It makes a fine show of glossy, deep green leaves beneath which are concealed the satin-purple spathes, the only indication of which is a penetrating stench of horse-dung! However the smell, which is in any case of short duration, is a small price to pay for an otherwise first-rate garden plant.

It is unfortunate that despite its distinctive appearance and fairly limited distribution, confusion surrounds the name *A. nigrum*. Vellozo (1827) published an illustration of a Brazilian aroid he named *Arum nigrum*. Vellozo's illustration, which doubtfully depicts *Alocasia plumbea* van Houtte (S. Mayo, pers. comm.), predates Schott's *A. nigrum* by 26 years. Prime (1980) evidently considered Vellozo's Brazilian epithet to have been validly published and this led him to rename the Yugoslavian *Arum*, using what he considered to be the next available name, *A. petteri* Schott. This however was an unnecessary name change. Vellozo's illustration lacks a pictorial analysis as required by the Code (ICBN Art. 42.2, 1988) for valid publication of a name based on an illustration alone. The name *Arum nigrum* Vellozo was thus not validly published and may be discounted (Mayo, pers. comm). Furthermore, *A. petteri* is not conspecific with *A. nigrum* Schott, and should in fact be referred to *A. orientale* Bieb. Prime's confusion on this point apparently arose because of a misidentification of Schott's material by Engler (1920).

Arum nigrum is separable from *A. orientale* by its far richer spathe coloration, shorter peduncle and noticeably more foetid smell. *Arum gratum* differs from *A. nigrum* by bearing its very pale purple, sweetly scented inflorescences at ground level.

Arum nigrum was originally thought to be restricted to the mountains of western Yugoslavia. Bornmüller (1927) and Rechinger (1943) reported the occurrence of the species on the Athos Peninsula, Greece, records that have been wrongly dismissed as *A. orientale*. More recently Akeroyd & Preston (1987) reported *A. nigrum* on the island of Samothraki in the northern Aegean, however, this record is of *A. elongatum*. Records from southern Italy are referable to *A. apulum*.

In cultivation, *A. nigrum* has proved to be a vigorous and hardy species, surviving the worst that a European winter can provide. For best results a rich, well-drained soil is needed, preferably in a shady, but not dark position. It is best to avoid planting in a place that receives early morning sun since the leaves, emerging in winter, can be severely damaged if they thaw too swiftly after a hard frost. Under glass a large clay pot will be needed, and a copious supply of both water and feed if the plant is to grow well.

Arum nigrum Schott in Oesterr. Bot. Wochenbl. 27: 213 (1857), & Icones Aroid. t.37, 38 (1857) & Prodr. Syst. Aroid., 81 (1860); Engler in A. & C. DC., Monogr. Phan. 2: 586–7 (1879); Hruby in Bull. Soc. Bot. Genève 4: 137 (1912); Engler, Pflanzenr. 73 (IV. 23F): 74–5 (1920). Type: Hort. Schönbrunn, *Schott* s.n. (holotype W, destroyed; isotype K!).

A. variolatum Schott, Prodr. Syst. Aroid., 81 (1860). Type: Cult. Schönbrunn. ex Dalmatia, *Maly* s.n. (holotype W, destroyed; lectotype selected here: Schott Icones Aroideae no. 1485, W!).

A. orientale Bieb. var. *nigrum* (Schott) Engler in A. & C. DC., Monogr. Phan. 2: 586 (1879).

A. orientale Bieb. var. *nigrum* (Schott) Engler forma *variolatum* (Schott) Engler, *op. cit.*, 587.

A. orientale Bieb. subsp. *nigrum* (Schott) Richter, Pl. Europ. 1: 172 (1890).

A. nigrum Schott var. *schottii* Engler, Pflanzenr. 73 (IV. 23F): 74 (1920). Type: as for *A. nigrum* Schott.

A. nigrum Schott var. *variolatum* (Schott) Engler, *op. cit.*, 75.

DESCRIPTION. *Tuberous herb* sprouting in spring from a discoid, vertical tuber 4–6 cm across, 2–2.5 cm thick. *Petioles* subterete, 11–22.5 cm long, 4–6 mm wide, deep green with slight purple staining basally. *Leaf-blade* sagittate-hastate to broadly sagittate, apex acute, 9.5–21 cm long, 7.5–18 cm wide, glossy deep green. *Inflorescence* smelling strongly of horse-dung. *Peduncle* much shorter than the leaves, terete, 5–9 cm long, 5–10 mm wide, bright mid-green. *Spathe* 12.5–20.5 cm long; spathe-tube oblong-cylindric, 4–5.5 cm long. 1.5–2.5 cm wide, constricted apically, exterior green basally, this colour extending c. ⅓ the way up the mid-vein, otherwise very dark purple, the margins darker still, interior pale green basally, darkening c. ½-way up to mid-green stained deep purple; spathe-limb broadly elliptic, 9–14 cm long, 3–8.5 cm wide, somewhat cucullate, minutely acuminate, externally glossy deep purple with greenish mottling towards the apex, interior deep purple. *Spadix* c. ½ as long as the spathe-limb, 8.5–13 cm in total length; appendix clavate to stoutly-cylindric, long-stipitate, 5.5–9.5 cm long, 5–10 mm wide, sooty purple, tinged with purple apically. *Staminodes* in 2 whorls forming a zone 2–4 mm long; bristles subulate, stiff, 5–7 mm long, violet to dark purple;

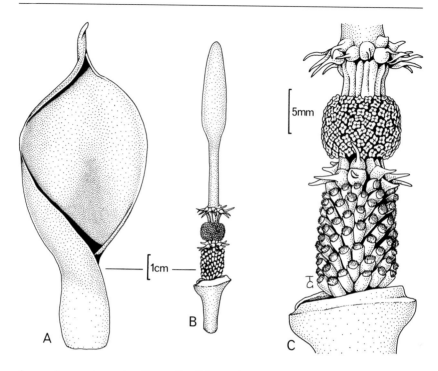

Arum nigrum. A, spathe; **B**, spadix; **C**, base of spadix.

bases bulbiform, verrucate, purplish yellow. *Interstices*: upper 2.5–3 mm long, ± smooth, dull yellow; lower 0.5–1 mm long, deeply and regularly longitudinally grooved, dull yellow, stained with purple. *Staminate flowers* in an oblong zone 8–9 mm long, 7–8 mm wide; anthers and connectives pale purple. *Pistillodes* in 1 whorl forming a zone 1–1.5 mm long; bristles subulate, stiff, 5–7 mm long, deep violet; bases massively conic, verrucate, dark yellow, stained with purple. *Pistillate flowers* in a cylindric cluster 13–15 mm long; ovaries oblong, 2.5–3 mm long, pale yellow, upper ⅓ violet; stigma pale grey-mauve. *Fruiting spike* oblong-cylindric, 3.5–5 cm long, 2–2.5 cm wide; berries pyriform, 3–9 mm long, 3–4 mm wide. *Germination* epigeal.

ILLUSTRATIONS. Grey-Wilson & Mathew, Bulbs, pl.35 (1981).

FLOWERING PERIOD. March to April.

HABITAT. Garrigue, amongst rocks in soil pockets, rocky hillsides; 250–800 m.

DISTRIBUTION. Yugoslavia (Dalmatia, Hercegovina, Montenegro), Greece (Athos, Jura, Skyros). MAP 10, p. 109.

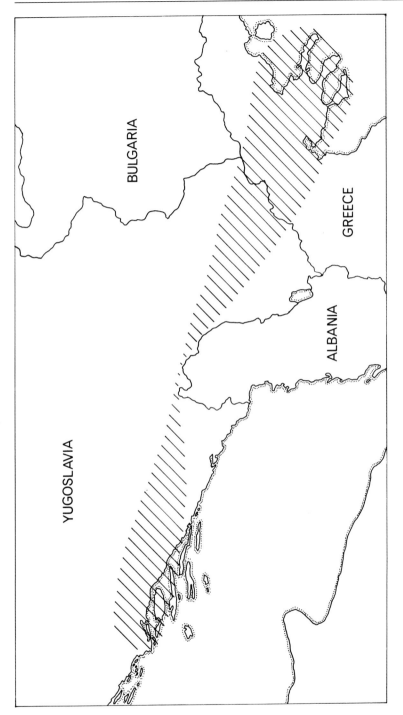

Map 10. Distribution of *Arum nigrum*.

11. ARUM CYRENAICUM

This lovely species was described by the Swiss botanist Hruby in 1912. Since then it has been re-collected on only a few occasions as herbarium material and twice as living plants. One of these live collections, made by Koenen in 1976, is the source of almost all the *A. cyrenaicum* presently in cultivation, although seed from a 1982 collection was offered recently by Munich Botanical Garden. More recently Briggs and Turland independently gathered material of *A. cyrenaicum* in southern Crete, the first records of the species outside Libya.

Arum cyrenaicum is similar to both *A. orientale* and *A. purpureospathum*, although it is distinct morphologically from either. *Arum cyrenaicum* is readily separable from *A. orientale* by the differently shaped staminate flower zone and sterile flowers, and from *A. purpureospathum* by the generally paler spathe and purple-stained, deep yellow, staminate flowers. In the wild *A. cyrenaicum* occurs in rocky places, either in the shade of large boulders or beneath low scrub, in Libya often in association with *Cyclamen rohlfsianum*. Due to the lack of field-work in Libya very little is known about the amount of variation that occurs in *A. cyrenaicum*. The clone in cultivation has a rather pale rosy purple spathe-limb compared with material gathered by Davis during the 1960s, which suggests that there is at least variation in colour. The Cretan material corresponds to the Davis collection. Libya's aroid flora is poorly known at present and the occurrence of other species of *Arum* cannot be ruled out.

Arum cyrenaicum has proved easy to grow if given frost-free conditions with an ample supply of water. There are at least two growers who have succeeded with this species out-of-doors by cultivating the plants in a bulb-frame which gives a free root-run. Under glass I have found that a hot, but not too dry, summer rest gives good results.

Arum cyrenaicum Hruby in Bull. Soc. Bot. Genève 4: 159 (1912); Engler Pflanzenr. 73 (IV. 23F): 81 (1920); El Gadi in Fl. Libya 41: 236 (1977). Type: Libya, Benghazi, Lethe, 9 March 1883, *Ruhmer* 320 (lectotype selected here, G!). Three syntypes are cited by Hruby (1912), *Ruhmer* 320, *Taubert* 363, *Taubert* 704, all in Geneva. Of these the Ruhmer collection is by far the best preserved, and thus the most suitable lectotype.

[*A. hygrophilum* var. *rupicola* sensu Durand & Barratte, Fl. Libya Prodr. 243 (1910), *non* Boiss. (1882).]

[*A. italicum* sensu Durand & Barratte, *op. cit.* 242, *non* Miller (1768).]

[*A. italicum* var. *byzantinum* sensu Durand & Barratte, *op. cit.* 243 (1910), *non* Engler (1879).]

DESCRIPTION. *Tuberous herb* sprouting in early autumn from a discoid, vertical tuber 3.5–5 cm across, 2–2.5 cm thick. *Petiole* terete, 5.5–27 cm long, 3–6 mm wide, dark green with moderate purple staining. *Leaf-blade* broadly sagittate, apex obtuse to rather bluntly acute, 8.5–20 cm long, 4–12 cm wide, semi-glossy deep green. *Inflorescence* smelling slightly of horse-dung. *Peduncle* not exceeding the leaves, terete, 3–11 cm long, 5–7 mm wide, semi-glossy mid-green, longitudinally striped with lighter green and moderately stained with purple. *Spathe* 10.5–16 cm long; spathe-tube oblong-cylindric, 2.5–4 cm

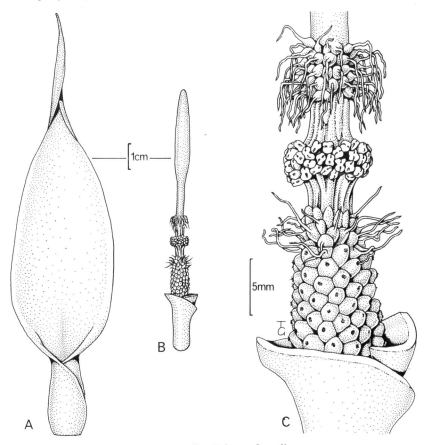

Arum cyrenaicum. **A**, spathe; **B**, spadix; **C**, base of spadix.

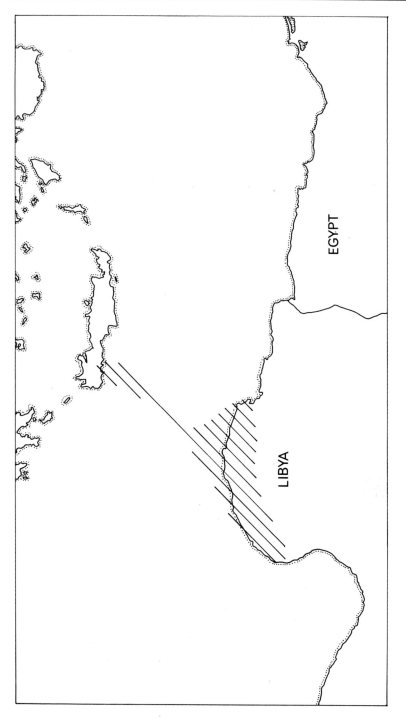

Map 11. Distribution of *Arum cyrenaicum*.

Plate 9

Arum rupicola var. *rupicola*

PANDORA SELLARS

Plate 10

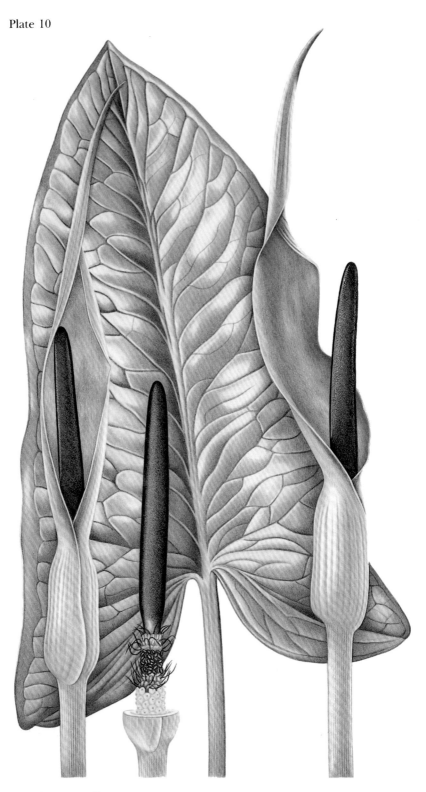

Arum jacquemontii

ANN FARRER

long, 2–2.5 cm wide, constricted apically, exterior pale green with a narrow dull purple margin, interior dark purple, fading to pale green basally and deepening to plum-purple apically; spathe-limb elliptic, 8.5–12 cm long, 4–5.5 cm wide, erect, the apex drooping forwards as the inflorescence ages, acuminate, externally greenish, flushed with purple towards the edges, interior pale rosy purple to dark purple, fading to pale purple towards the tube and apex, limb green at the tip. *Spadix c.* ½ as long as the spathe-limb, 7–9.5 cm in total length; appendix slender-clavate, long-stipitate, 3.5–6.5 cm long, 5–7 mm wide, deep purple with a slight olive-green tinge, stipe darker. *Staminodes* in 3 or 4 whorls, forming a zone 4–6 mm long; bristles filiform, flexuous, 6–7 mm long, cream, minutely tipped with purple; bases pyriform, slightly verrucate, cream, with the verrucae tipped with lilac-mauve. *Interstices*: upper 4–5 mm long, lower 3.5–4 mm long, both longitudinally ridged, cream. *Staminate flowers* in a cylindric zone 2.5–3 mm long, 7–8 mm wide; anthers and connectives deep yellow, thecae with dull purple staining along the edges. *Pistillodes* in 2 or 3 whorls forming a zone 5–6 mm long; bristles filiform, flexuous, 5–6 mm long, cream, minutely tipped with purple; bases pyriform, slightly verrucate, cream, the verrucae tipped with lilac-mauve. *Pistillate flowers* in an oblong-cylindric cluster 1–2 cm long, 6.5–7 mm wide; ovaries oblong, truncate apically, mid-cream; stigma cream. *Fruiting spike* short-cylindric, 2.5–4 cm long, 2–2.5 cm wide; berries pyriform, 4–9 mm long, 3–5 mm wide. *Germination* epigeal.

ILLUSTRATIONS. PLATE 6. No other good illustrations traced.

FLOWERING PERIOD. March to April.

HABITAT. Open scrub, amongst boulders, shady slopes; 20–350 m.

DISTRIBUTION. NE Libya (Cyrenaica), Greece (S Crete). MAP 11, p. 112.

12. ARUM PURPUREOSPATHUM

The discovery of a new species is always a satisfying event, especially when the species turns out to be one of the most attractive members of the genus yet found. The first record I saw of this plant was a slide of an unidentified *Arum* taken by Vaughn Fleming in south-western Crete. The slide depicted a plant with a glistening purple spathe, much brighter in colour than any known species. Later Vaughn gave me the exact locality of the colony and in April 1985 I re-collected the plant in Crete. With sufficient material to hand it became apparent that the species was related to the *A. cyrenaicum* but distinctive enough to be recognized as new (Boyce, 1987a).

Arum purpureospathum and *A. cyrenaicum* are clearly related by their long-stipitate, clavate spadix-appendices, purple spathe-limb

113

interiors and by producing only a slight smell of horse-dung. *Arum purpureospathum* is readily distinguished from the Libyan plant by its far more intense spathe colour, uniformly deep purple spathe-tube interior, black-purple rather than cream upper interstice, pale mauve sterile flowers, quadratic male flower zone and longer female flower zone.

The type locality of *A. purpureospathum* is restricted in area and although the species is quite plentiful, there is a very real threat of despoilment by collectors. For this reason the exact locality will not be stated here. Since publishing the description other, discrete, sites have been discovered by Mary Briggs and Nicholas Turland. The plants in these new localities differ from those at the type locality by having much shorter and more slender spadix-appendices and a cream rather than black-purple upper interstice. Photographs taken in the general area of the site also suggest that the spathe colour may vary somewhat as well, with some plants displaying a dull, rather pale purple spathe-limb. However, in my opinion the plants are sufficiently similar not to warrant taxonomic recognition.

In cultivation it appears that plants in pots will not withstand frost for any length of time, but once planted out *A. purpureospathum* appears to be reasonably hardy. From the original collection the plant has multiplied well both vegetatively and from seed and is now well established in a number of collections.

Arum purpureospathum Boyce in Aroideana 10: 8 (1987), Turland in Bull. Alpine Gard. Soc. 57: 112–117 (1989). Type: Southwestern Crete, 6 April 1985, *Boyce* 51 (holotype K!).

DESCRIPTION. *Tuberous herb* sprouting in early to mid-autumn from a discoid, vertical tuber 4–7 cm across, 2–3 cm thick. *Petiole* D-shaped in cross-section, 12–20 cm long, 3–5 mm wide, deep green longitudinally streaked with purple, the basal ⅓ stained with the same colour. *Leaf-blade* sagittate-hastate, apex acute to rounded, 14–22 cm long, 11–17 cm wide, light to mid-green, glossy. *Inflorescence* smelling weakly of horse-dung. *Peduncle* shorter than the leaves, terete, 12–15 cm long, 5–6 mm wide, upper ½ mid-green with purple streaks, lower half purple. *Spathe* 23–30 cm long; spathe-tube oblong-cylindric, 5–7 cm long, 1.75–2.5 cm wide, tapering and constricted apically, exterior mid-green longitudinally striped with purple, and stained with purple above, interior uniformly deep purple; spathe-limb broadly lanceolate, 18–23 cm long, 5–9 cm wide, erect apart from the apical 3–4 cm which droops forward, long-acuminate, externally deep green basally,

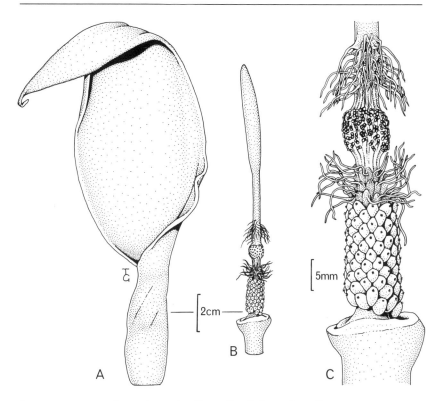

Arum purpureospathum. **A**, spathe; **B**, spadix; **C**, base of spadix.

remainder deep purple, shiny, internally mid-purple or dull to deep bright purple, ± lustrous, rarely somewhat matt. *Spadix* ⅓–½ as long as the spathe-limb, 6–12.5 cm in total length; appendix clavate-cylindric, long-stipitate, obtuse, 3–5 cm long, 2.5–5 mm wide, black-purple. *Staminodes* in 3 whorls forming a zone 3–8 mm long; bristles filiform, flexuous, 6–11 mm long, pale mauve; bases conic, verrucate, deep purple, occasionally paler. *Interstices*: upper 3–6 mm long, longitudinally ridged, black-purple to cream; lower 1–3 mm long, cream, with scattered rudimentary and ± fully developed staminodes. *Staminate flowers* in a quadratic zone 4–7 mm long, 5–9 mm wide; anthers black-purple, connectives whitish cream. *Pistillodes* in *c.* 3 whorls forming a zone 3–5 mm long; bristles filiform, flexuous, 9–10 mm long, pale mauve; bases elongate-pyriform, smooth, black-purple. *Pistillate flowers* in a cylindric cluster 15–20 mm long, 7–10 mm wide; ovaries barrel-shaped, 2.5–3.5 mm long, pale green with a cream apex; stigma cream tinged with brown. *Fruiting spike* oblong-cylindric, 6.5–8 cm long, 2.5–3 cm wide; berries pyriform 6–11 mm long, 5–6 mm wide. *Germination* epigeal.

ILLUSTRATIONS. PLATE 7. Bull. Alpine Gard. Soc. 54: 37 (1986).

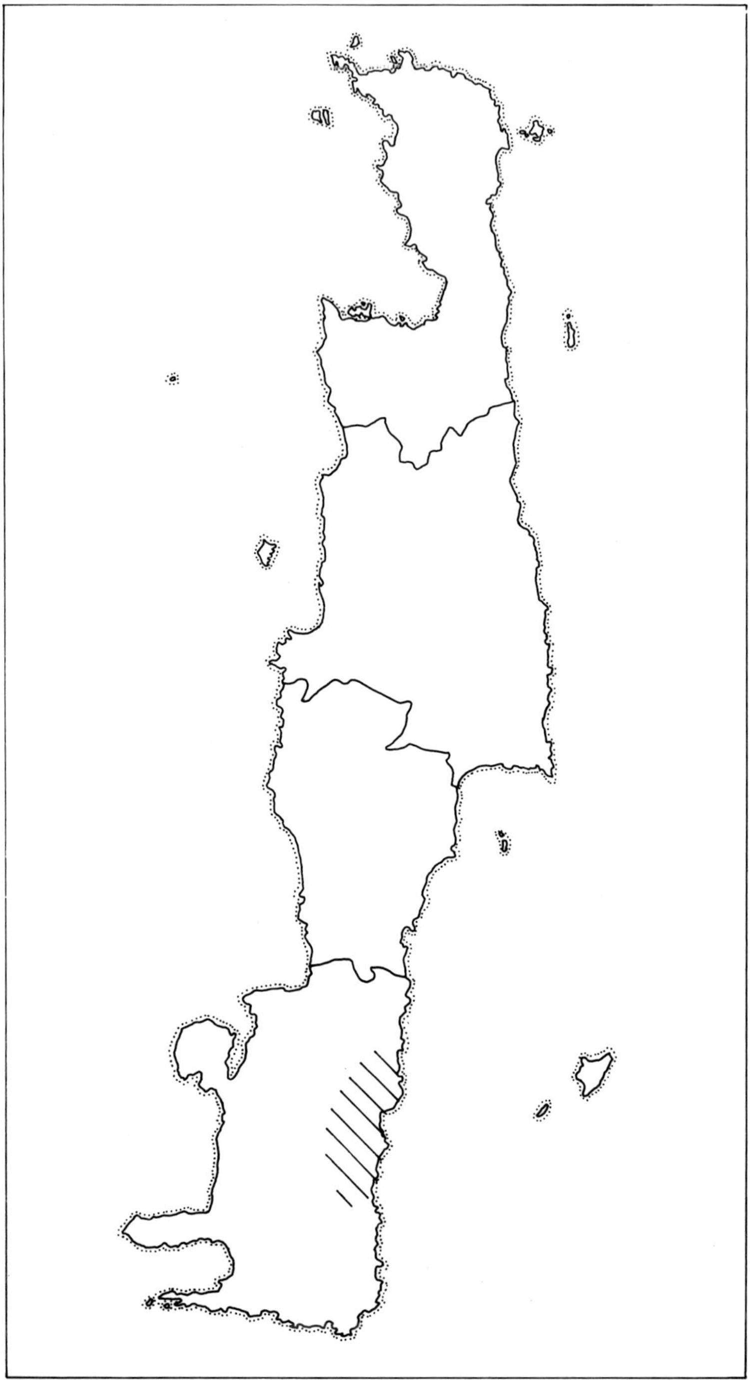

Map 12. Distribution of *Arum purpureospathum*.

FLOWERING PERIOD. March to April.

HABITAT. In short grass and among large stones, rarely on bare rocky hillsides or in garrigue; sea-level to 100 m.

DISTRIBUTION. Greece (SW Crete). MAP 12, p. 116.

13. ARUM BALANSANUM

Arum balansanum is an interesting species allied to both A. hainesii and A. orientale by virtue of the cylindric, stipitate spadix-appendix, purple staminate flowers and purple-washed spathes low down amongst the petioles. Arum balansanum is readily distinguishable from A. orientale by its paler, more or less white spathe-tube interior and different arrangement and colour of the sterile flowers. It differs from A. hainesii by the shorter, more slender spadix-appendix and spathe-limb, together with the purple spathe-limb interior and a different configuration of the flowers.

Until recently A. balansanum had not been introduced as living material, indeed, herbarium material was at a premium even in Turkish institutions. However, due to the work of David Drummond, who is currently investigating pollination vectors in Arum, a number of living collections and a good quantity of pressed material is now available for study.

To date A. balansanum has proved easy to grow and should prove to be hardy outdoors in the British Isles, since gatherings of A. rupicola from the same region are thriving outdoors in a number of private collections.

Arum balansanum R. Mill in Notes Roy. Bot. Gard. Edinb. 41: 45 (1983); Mill in Davis, Fl. Turkey 8: 48–49 (1984); Mill & Alpinar in Davis, Fl. Turkey 10: 218 (1988). Type: Turkey, Uşak, Yachamichlar-Keui, à 8 km au nord d'Ouchak (Phrygie), 3 June 1857, Balansa 60 (holotype G-BOIS!; isotypes G-DELESS! K! P!).
[A. phrygium Boiss., Fl. Orient. 5: 39 (1882); Tchiat., Asie Min. Bot. 2: 648 (1860), nom. nud.]

DESCRIPTION. *Tuberous herb* sprouting in early autumn from a discoid, vertically orientated tuber, 3.5–6 cm across, 2–2.5 cm thick. *Petiole* 13–23.5 cm long, 3–4.5 mm wide, dark to mid-green. *Leaf-blade* oblong-hastate, 8–14 cm long, 3.5–10 cm wide, apex acuminate, dark to mid-green. *Inflorescence* smelling of horse-dung. *Peduncle* subequal to the leaves, terete, 13–26 cm

117

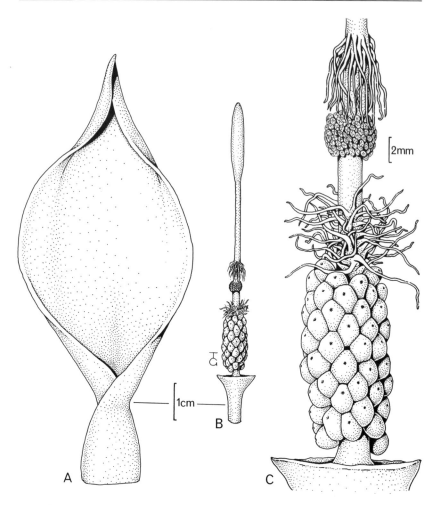

Arum balansanum. **A**, spathe; **B**, spadix; **C**, base of spadix.

long, 3–4 mm wide, mid-green. *Spathe* 9–14 cm long; spathe-tube oblong-cylindric, somewhat inflated, 2–3.5 cm long, 1–1.5 cm wide, constricted apically, exterior mid-green, interior white; spathe-limb narrowly lanceolate to lanceolate-elliptic, 7–10.5 cm long, 1–3.5 cm wide, erect, acuminate, externally pale green, internally pale green to purple. *Spadix* extending less than ½-way up the spathe-limb or subequal to it, 4–7 cm in total length; appendix slender-cylindric, indistinctly stipitate, 2–5 cm long, 2–3.5 mm wide, purple, stipe paler. *Staminodes* in 3 whorls forming a zone 4.5–5 mm long; bristles filiform, flexuous, 3.5–6.5 mm long, whitish yellow; bases elongate-conic, smooth, cream. *Interstices*: upper 3–3.5 mm long, minutely

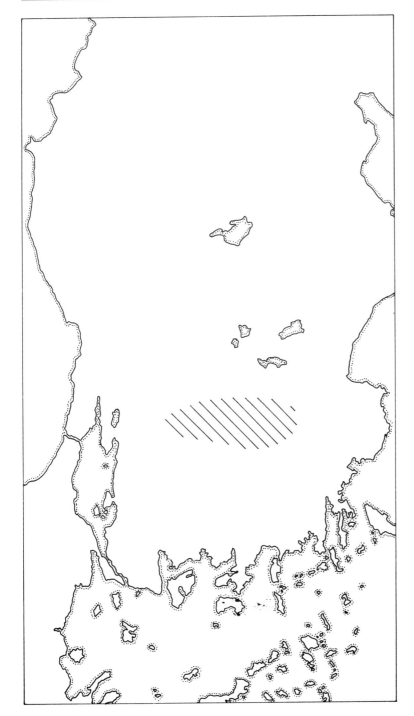

Map 13. Distribution of *Arum balansanum.*

119

longitudinally ridged, cream; lower 3–4 mm long, with a few scattered vestigial pistillode bases, cream. *Staminate flowers* in a ± quadratic zone 2.5–3 mm long, 3–3.5 mm wide; anthers and connectives purple. *Pistillodes* in 4 or 5 whorls forming a zone 4–4.5 mm long; bristles filiform, flexuous, 2–6 mm long, whitish yellow; bases barely swollen, smooth, cream. *Pistillate flowers* in an oblong-cylindric cluster 10–17 mm long, ovaries oblong, flattened apically, 2–2.5 mm long, cream with a purple apex; stigma cream. *Fruiting spike* unknown. *Germination* unknown.

ILLUSTRATIONS. Not traced.

FLOWERING PERIOD. May to June.

HABITAT. Deciduous woodland, shady gullies; 1,100–1,200 m.

DISTRIBUTION. Turkey (SW Anatolia). MAP 13, p. 119.

14. ARUM HAINESII

The specimen that eventually became the type of *Arum haineseii* was collected in 1961 in north-west Iraq by Agnew and Hadač, who found it growing in a 'shady date and orange garden' at Ba'quba. The name *A. hainesii* was given to the material by them soon afterwards, but not described until 1981 by Harald Riedl. In this paper Riedl commented that *A. hainesii* appeared to be allied to *A. conophalloides* (i.e. *A. rupicola*) but differed in having a shorter, more distinctly stipitate spadix-appendix and more numerous, densely arranged staminodes. Riedl also noted the similarity of the staminodes of *A. hainesii* to those of *A. hygrophilum*, suggesting that this might indicate a relationship. Ecologically *A. hygrophilum* and *A. hainesii* are distinct, with the former occurring in permanently damp conditions while *A. hainesii* is found in seasonally dry cultivated land. Apart from the similarities of the staminodes there are no distinct features in common between the two species. In my opinion *A. hainesii* lies closest to *A. elongatum* and *A. balansanum*. All three species carry their inflorescences beneath, or just level with, the foliage, and display a stipitate, rather stout spadix-appendix and densely arranged staminodes. Furthermore, all occur in seasonal habitats.

Arum hainesii had only been known until recently from the type gathering. However, a second and earlier collection has come to light at the Herbarium of the Royal Botanic Garden, Edinburgh and a third at the Botanical Institute, Munich. The Edinburgh collection is a fruiting specimen.

To date no living material of *A. hainesii* has been introduced into

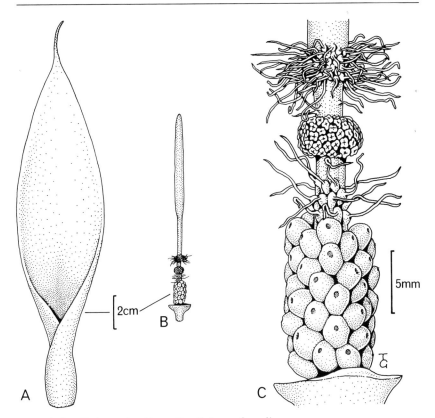

Arum hainesii. **A**, spathe; **B**, spadix; **C**, base of spadix.

cultivation. Although the herbarium specimens available are complete and in good condition the relationships of this intriguing species will not be fully understood until studies of living plants have been made.

Arum hainesii Agnew & Hadač ex H. Riedl in Kew Bull. 36: 643 (1981); Riedl in Townsend & Guest, Flora of Iraq 8: 192 (1985). Type: Iraq, Baquba, shady date and orange garden, 9 May 1961, *A.D.Q. Agnew & E. Hadač* 3581 (holotype K!).

DESCRIPTION. *Tuberous herb* sprouting (in autumn?) from a discoid, vertically orientated tuber 3–6 cm across, 2–2.5 cm thick. *Petiole* terete, 45–60 cm long, 4–5 mm wide, mid-green, paler basally. *Leaf-blade* hastate, apex acute to slightly obtuse, 10–33 cm long, 8.5–24 cm wide, dull mid-green. *Inflorescence* scent unknown. *Peduncle* much shorter than the leaves, terete,

121

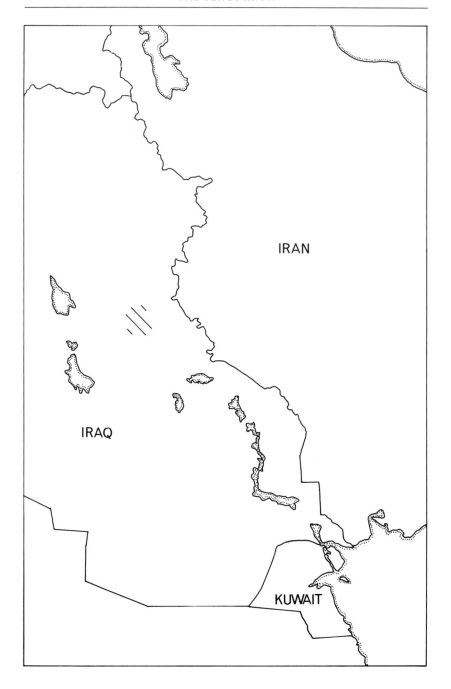

Map 14. Distribution of *Arum hainesii*.

8–10 cm long, 3–4 mm wide, mid-green. *Spathe* 15.5–25 cm long: spathe-tube cylindric, 3.5–4 cm long, 2–2.5 cm wide, constricted apically, exterior pale green, interior paler, usually suffused with purple; spathe-limb lanceolate, 12–21 cm long, 2.5–4.5 cm wide, erect, acuminate, externally and internally pale green. *Spadix* less than ½ as long as the spathe-limb, up to 13 cm in total length; appendix cylindric, stipitate, 4.5–5.5 cm long, 4–4.5 mm wide, pale brown, slightly farinose (artifact of drying ?). *Staminodes* in 5 whorls forming a zone 4–5 mm long; bristles filiform, flexuous, 7–8 mm long, pale cream; bases bulbiform, smooth, dull cream. *Interstices*: upper 2.5 mm long, ± smooth, cream; lower 2 mm long, longitudinally ridged, cream. *Staminate flowers* in an oblong zone 2 mm long, 5 mm wide; anthers and connectives dark purple. *Pistillodes* in 3 or 4 whorls forming a zone 2.5–3 mm long; bristles filiform, flexuous, 4–5 mm long, pale cream; bases compressed-semiglobose, smooth, cream. *Pistillate flowers* in a cylindric cluster 8–10 mm long, 3–4 mm wide; ovaries oblong, truncate, 2–2.25 mm long, pale yellow, purple apically; stigma cream. *Fruiting spike* oblong-cylindric, *c.* 4 cm long, 1.5 cm wide; berries ovoid, 4.5–9 mm long, 3–3.5 mm wide. *Germination* not known.

ILLUSTRATIONS. None traced.

FLOWERING PERIOD. May.

HABITAT. To date known only from cultivated ground; *c.* 40 m.

DISTRIBUTION. Eastern Iraq. MAP 14, p. 122.

15. ARUM ELONGATUM

This attractive species, although apparently common in its native habitat is seldom seen in cultivation. This is undoubtedly due to the inaccessibility of its habitat rather than to any difficulty in cultivation since *A. elongatum* is easily grown and perfectly hardy. All that is required is a moist, sunny position.

Described by the Finnish botanist Steven, *A. elongatum* was originally collected at Nikita on the Crimean Peninsula, and for many years was considered to occur only in this restricted area. Gradually, records of the occurrence of similar plants in the Balkans and northern Greece (Rechinger, 1943), revealed that in fact *A. elongatum* has a wider range than at first supposed. Recently, material from northern Turkey has proved to belong to this species (Mill & Alpinar, 1988) and it is now apparent that the species has a natural range covering the area to the north and north-east of the Black Sea, spreading as far south as the island of Samothraki in the northern Aegean (Akeroyd, pers. comm.). The records of *A. elongatum* in Israel

(Braverman & Koach, 1982; Koach, 1986) are referable to *A. rupicola*; *A. elongatum* is absent from the Middle East.

Arum elongatum is related to *A. orientale* by the bicoloured spathe-tube interior, stipitate spadix-appendix, dung-smelling, 'cryptic' inflorescences and arrangement of the sterile flowers. It is distinguished from *A. orientale* by the longer, stouter, shortly stipitate spadix-appendix, which is distinctly constricted at a point about a third of its length above the base. Additionally the spathe-limb of *A. elongatum* is generally elliptic-lanceolate, rather pointed and rich maroon-purple in contrast to the broader, somewhat blunt, pale greenish purple spathe-limb typical of *A. orientale*. The two species also differ ecologically: *A. elongatum* is invariably associated with moist, open deciduous forest or amongst rocks along the edges of coniferous woodland, whereas *A. orientale* generally occurs in rather dry woodland or in scrubby, rocky areas.

Apart from being treated as a distinct species, *A. elongatum* has also been combined with *A. orientale* at various ranks (Engler, 1879; 1920). However, the morphological and ecological features outlined above support the separation of the taxa. In addition, a number of other species have, in the past, been combined with *A. elongatum* at various ranks. Most recently Riedl (1963) treated both *A. detruncatum* and *A. engleri* as subspecies of *A. elongatum*. Study of both living and herbarium material has convinced me that these combinations do not reflect the true relationship between *A. elongatum*, *A. detruncatum* and *A. engleri*.

Arum detruncatum has been the subject of much confusion and misidentification since its publication. Examination of the material available led Mill & Alpinar (1988) to the conclusion that *A. conophalloides* was inseparable from *A. detruncatum*. I have taken this a stage further in treating both species as synonyms of the earlier, and little known name, *A. rupicola*. A full discussion of *A. detruncatum*, together with a reassessment of *A. engleri*, is given under *A. rupicola*.

The recently described *A. elongatum* subsp. *alpinariae* is as yet too poorly understood for its taxonomic position to be properly established. The single collection known is decidedly distinct morphologically from subsp. *elongatum*. I suspect that subsp. *alpinariae* may prove to be a distinct species, but in the absence of further collections, the subspecific rank used by Mill & Alpinar (1988) is retained.

124

Arum elongatum Steven in Bull. Bot. Soc. Mosc. 32 (2): 67 (1857); Schott, Prodr. Syst. Aroid., 100 (1860); Hruby in Bull. Soc. Bot. Genève 4: 140 (1912). Type: Crimea, circa Nikitam, *Steven* s.n. (holotype LE; isotype G!).

DESCRIPTION. *Tuberous herb* sprouting in autumn from a discoid, vertically orientated tuber, 3–7 cm across, 1.5–3 cm thick. *Petiole* terete, 14–45 cm long, 2.5–9 mm wide, dark green. *Leaf-blade* sagittate-hastate to oblong-hastate, apex acute, 7–32 cm long, 3.5–21 cm wide, dark green. *Inflorescence* strongly foetid of horse-dung and urine. *Peduncle* much shorter than, to just equalling, the leaves, terete, 4.5–14 cm long, 3.5–9 mm wide, mid-green. *Spathe* 13.5–27 cm long; spathe-tube oblong-cylindric, constricted apically, 2–5 cm long, 1.5–2 cm wide, exterior pale to mid-green, stained with maroon-purple especially along the margin, interior greenish white below, mid-purple above; spathe-limb lanceolate to oblong-lanceolate or ovate-triangular, acute to acuminate, erect, 12.5–25 cm long, 2.5–10 cm wide, externally dull mid-green ± stained with dark purple along the margin and at the apex, internally dark purple or crimson, darker towards the margin and apex. *Spadix* slightly shorter to less than ½ as long as the spathe-limb, 6.5–26 cm in total length; appendix stoutly cylindric and constricted *c*. ⅓ of its length above the base in subsp. *elongatum*, slender-clavate. in subsp. *alpinariae*, briefly but distinctly stipitate or long-stipitate, 4–23 cm long, 4.5–11 mm wide, dark maroon-purple, stipe paler or darker. *Staminodes* in 3 or 4 whorls forming a zone 3.5–4 mm long; bristles filiform, flexuous, 3–4 mm long, mid-yellow; stained with purple especially towards the tip (subsp. *elongatum*), or white and unstained (subsp. *alpinariae*); bases conic to slightly swollen, slightly to markedly verrucate, mid-yellow. *Interstices*: upper 3–3.5 mm long, longitudinally ridged, sometimes with scattered vestigial staminode bases, pale yellow; lower 2–3.5 mm long, longitudinally ridged, sometimes with scattered pistillode bases, pale yellow. *Staminate flowers* in a roughly oblong zone 3.5–5.6 mm long, 3–4.5 mm wide; anthers and connectives dull yellow ± stained with deep purple. *Pistillodes* in 2 or 3 whorls forming a zone 3–3.5 mm long; bristles filiform, flexuous, 0.5–5 mm long, mid-yellow, stained with purple especially towards the apex (subsp. *elongatum*) or white and unstained (subsp. *alpinariae*); bases conic, slightly to markedly verrucate, mid-yellow. *Pistillate flowers* in an oblong-cylindric cluster 9–13 mm long, ovaries oblong, 2–2.5 mm long, pale greenish yellow stained with deep purple apically; stigma pale grey. *Fruiting spike* (in subsp. *elongatum*) oblong-cylindric, 5–6 cm long, 3–3.5 cm wide when mature; berries oblong-pyriform, 5–11 mm long, 3.5–5 mm wide. The fruiting spike of subsp. *alpinariae* is unknown. *Germination* unknown.

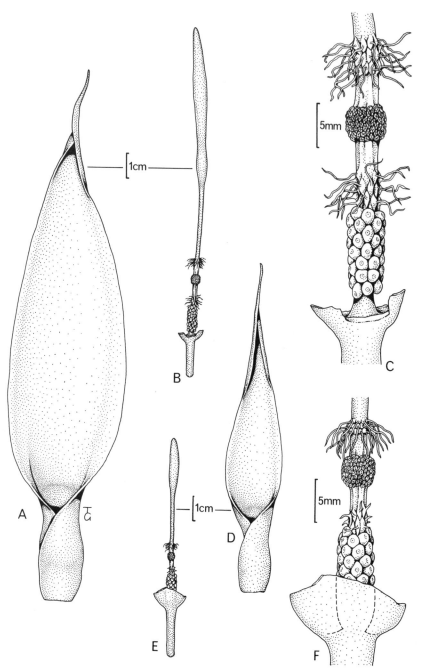

Arum elongatum subsp. **elongatum**: **A**, spathe; **B**, spadix; **C**, base of spadix. Subsp. **alpinariae**: **D**, spathe; **E**, spadix; **F**, base of spadix.

126

Key to the Subspecies

1. Spadix-appendix ± stoutly cylindric, ¾ as long to subequal to the spathe-limb; spathe-limb interior dark purple   **a.** subsp. **elongatum**
   Spadix-appendix slender-clavate, *c.* ½ as long as the spathe-limb; spathe-limb interior crimson   **b.** subsp. **alpinariae**

a. subsp. elongatum

A. orientale Bieb. var. *elongatum* (Steven) Engler in A. & C. DC., Monogr. Phan. 2: 587 (1879).

A. orientale Bieb. subsp. *elongatum* (Steven) Engler, Pflanzenr. 73 (IV. 23F): 79 (1920).

A. orientale Bieb. subsp. *elongatum* (Steven) Engler var. *stevenii* Engler, *loc. cit., nom. illeg.* Type: as for *A. elongatum* Steven.

A. orientale Bieb. subsp. *elongatum* (Steven) Engler var. *stevenii* Engler subvar. *depauperatum* Engler, *loc. cit.* Type: Turkey, Pontus australis, montis Yildis-Dagh, 1,200 m, 9 June 1890, *Bornmüller* 2546 (B!). (Lectotype selected here. Of the numerous syntypes listed by Engler this is the only sheet extant at Berlin.)

A. orientale Bieb. subsp. *elongatum* (Steven) Engler var. *stevenii* Engler subvar. *pleiocyclum* Engler, *loc. cit.* Type: none of the syntypes listed by Engler remains in Berlin and since I have been unable to locate any material that agrees with the protologue for this taxon, neotypification is not possible.

DESCRIPTION. As in key.

ILLUSTRATIONS. PLATE 8. Takhtadjan in Takhtadjan, Zhizn' Rast. (Tsvetk. Rast.) 6: t.2, facing page 465 (1982).

FLOWERING PERIOD. April to early June.

HABITAT. Deciduous woodland, edges of coniferous woodland, scrubby hillsides; 250–750 m.

DISTRIBUTION. Bulgaria, Greece, N Turkey, Belorussia. MAP 15a, p. 128.

Subsp. *elongatum* is a plant worthy of, but rarely seen in, cultivation. Virtually none of the material offered commercially in the British Isles is correctly identified. There are collections true to name in amateur collections and seed obtained from amateur enthusiasts is usually correctly identified.

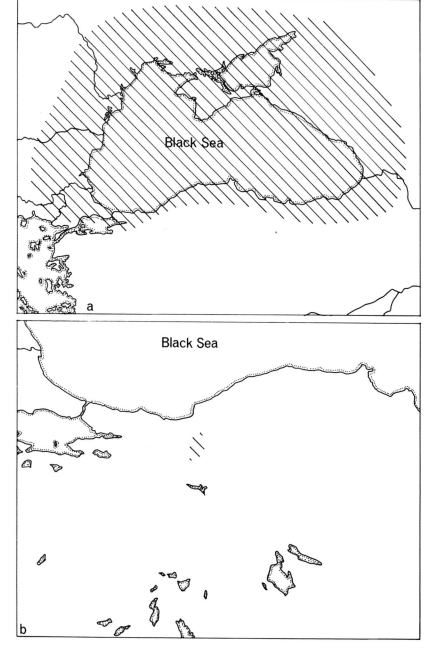

Map 15. Distribution of *Arum elongatum*. a: subsp. *elongatum*. b: subsp. *alpinariae*.

Plate 11

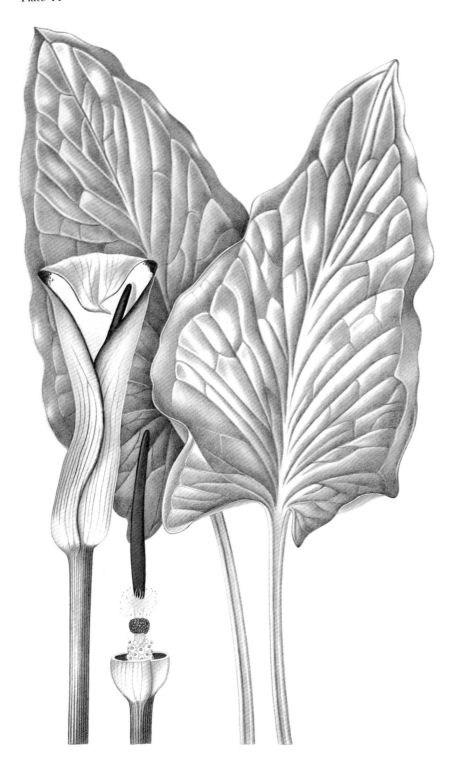

Arum euxinum

ANN FARRER

Plate 12

Arum hygrophilum

PANDORA SELLARS

b. subsp. **alpinariae** K. Alpinar & R. Mill in Davis, Fl. Turkey 10: 236 (1988). Type: Turkey, Sebsen to Bolu, Bolu Yolu, Ağu Daği, Kesik yaylasi, among *Juniperus*, 1,600 m, 6 June 1983, *K. Alpinar* (ISTE 50605 (holotype ISTE! isotypes E! K – photograph!).

DESCRIPTION. As in key.
ILLUSTRATIONS. None at present.
FLOWERING PERIOD. June.
HABITAT. Juniper scrub; 1,600 m.
DISTRIBUTION. N Turkey (Bölü). MAP 15b, p. 128.

Subsp. *alpinariae* is a very attractive plant; its bright crimson spathe-limb is unique in the genus. The only gathering to date originates from a botanically fascinating area of Turkey which has yielded a number of interesting *Arum* species.

c. Subsection Tenuifila

Arum subsection **Tenuifila** (Engler) Boyce in Kew Bull. 44: 391 (1989).
Arum § *Tenuifila* Engler, Pflanzenr. 73 (IV. 23F): 68 (1920), rankless taxon (see Boyce, 1989). Lectotype: *A. rupicola* Boiss. (selected by Boyce in Kew Bull. 44: 391, 1989).

Peduncles longer than petioles. *Spadix-appendix* shortly stipitate or sessile, slender to stout, occasionally massive. *Staminodes and pistillodes* with long, filiform, flexuous bristles. *Spathe-tube* interior wholly purple. *Inflorescence* scentless.

16. ARUM RUPICOLA

Horticulturists often complain that the names of well-known plants have changed 'yet again'. In fact, the number of cases in which the names of cultivated plants have been changed is quite small compared with the total number of cultivated species. Occasionally, however, name changes are unavoidable. In the present case the adoption of the obscure name *A. rupicola* for the familiar *A. conophalloides* is necessary both because of improved understanding of the taxonomy and the nomenclatural rule of priority.

Throughout Asia Minor, *A. rupicola* is one of the commonest *Arum* species, often abundant on rocky hillsides usually at moderate altitudes. In Turkey and Iran, and also in the population recently discovered by Lance Chilton on the Aegean island of Lesbos, *A. rupicola* usually displays a massive conic-cylindric spadix-appendix borne on a short, rather stout stipe; this form is the plant known as *A. conophalloides*. Towards the Turkish border with Syria, the spadix-appendix is often much more slender with a rather poorly defined stipe; this is the plant described as *A. rupicola*. Plants intermediate in spadix-appendix size have been called *A. detruncatum*. In most populations of *A. rupicola* the spathe colour is predominantly purple, with the spadix-appendix usually a shade darker. However, scattered populations in which the spathe-limb is pale greenish white and the spadix-appendix grey-lilac can be found almost throughout the entire range of the species. The Lesbos colony has several individuals with remarkable mid-brown spathes and spadix-appendices. This type of coloration has not previously been observed. Although extremes of shape and size are distinctive, a thorough study of many populations reveals a complete range of grading linking the extreme forms. It is this continuity of variation that has led me to treat *A. conophalloides*, *A. detruncatum* and *A. rupicola* as all belonging to the same species.

Arum rupicola is closest to *A. korolkowii* and *A. jacquemontii*. All three species share an unscented 'flag' inflorescence, a spadix-appendix usually equalling the spathe-limb in length, slender sterile flowers and a white spathe-tube interior. *Arum rupicola* differs from *A. korolkowii* in having concolorous green, not striped, petioles, in lacking the distinctive mid-green spathe-limb, in having smoother pistillode and staminode bases, a more robust habit, and in possessing spinulose, not scabrose, pollen exine. The similarities between *A. rupicola* and *A. jacquemontii* are more marked since both typically display purple inflorescences. However, *A. jacquemontii* differs in its unique deep purple pistillode and staminode bases, its emergence later in the year and dull purple rather than green shoots and petioles.

Apart from these species, there are possibly others involved. *Arum engleri*, described from Iran, has been sunk previously into *A. elongatum* (Riedl, 1963). However, the long peduncle (in relation to the petioles), white spathe-tube interior, short-stipitate spadix-appendix and scentless inflorescence all indicate that *A. engleri* is more closely allied to *A. rupicola* than to *A. elongatum*. Comparison of *A. engleri* and *A. rupicola* has revealed no characters that can be used to

130

differentiate between them. *Arum engleri* is accordingly here reduced to synonymy.

Arum kotschyi is more problematic. Little material exists of this species, but the type specimen appears to be different from *A. rupicola*. The most striking feature of the Geneva type specimen is the remarkably slender spadix-appendix. In addition, the spathe-tube is rather wide and lacks the marked apical constriction present in *A. rupicola*. I suspect that *A. kotschyi* may well prove to be a species distinct from *A. rupicola*, but prefer to wait until more material becomes available. Another species that may require reappraisal with the availability of more material is the recently described *A. giganteum*. In the description the major distinguishing feature used by Ghahreman (1983) is the size of the plant, which is up to 120 cm tall. More important, however, is the statement that the spathe-limb does not open fully. This, if correctly reported, is unique in the genus and would certainly further support the maintenance of *A. giganteum* as a distinct species.

Arum rupicola Boiss., Diagn. 1 (13): 7 (1853); Schott, Syn. Aroid., 14 (1856) & Prodr. Syst. Aroid., 96 (1860); Engler in A. & C. DC., Monogr. Phan. 2: 588 (1879). Type: Syria, in cavis umbrosis rupium Antilibani ad septentrionem spectantibus inter Zebdani et Zachle. Legi floriferum fine Maii, 1845, *Boissier* s.n. (holotype G!).

DESCRIPTION. *Tuberous herb* sprouting in early winter from a discoid, vertically orientated tuber 4–8 cm across, 2–3.5 cm thick. *Petiole* terete, 10–55 cm long, 3–6 mm wide, pale to mid-green. *Leaf-blade* oblong-sagittate to oblong-hastate, apex subacute to obtuse, occasionally rounded, 8–25 cm long, 4–18.5 cm wide, mid-green. *Inflorescence* odourless. *Peduncle* exceeding the leaves, terete, 10–65 cm long, 4–12 mm wide, pale to mid-green. *Spathe* 11.5–40 cm long; spathe-tube oblong cylindric, 2–7 cm long, 0.75–2.5 cm wide, moderately to strongly constricted apically, exterior pale to mid-green, very rarely mid-brown, sometimes with purple staining along the margin at the top, interior white; spathe-limb linear-lanceolate to lanceolate, 9.5–33 cm long, 2–8 cm wide, erect at first but soon flopping either backwards or forwards and curling apically, margins sometimes crispate, acute to acuminate, externally pale to mid-green, often heavily stained with purple along the margin, sometimes ± entirely purple, rarely entirely green, very rarely mid-brown, internally pale greenish white ± stained with deep purple or maroon, more rarely greenish white with a very narrow purple margin, very rarely mid-brown. *Spadix* subequal to or exceeding the spathe-limb, 8–33 cm

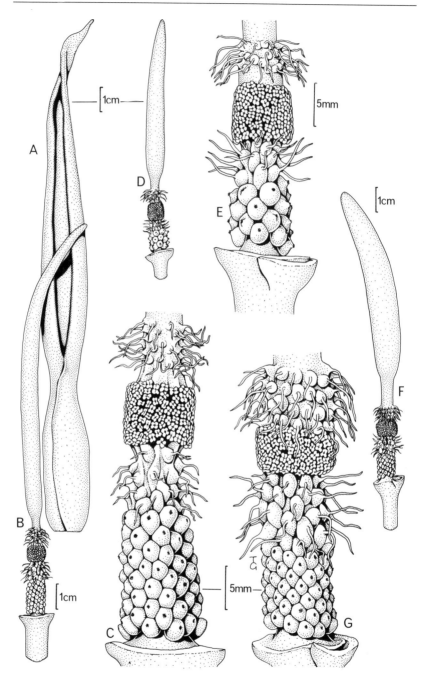

Arum rupicola. **A**, spathe, from clone referable to *A. conophalloides sensu stricto*; **B**, spadix, from clone referable to *A. rupicola sensu stricto*; **C**, base of spadix, from clone

in total length; appendix cylindric to conic-cylindric, sometimes massively so, short-stipitate to almost stalkless, 6–32 cm long, 13–25 mm wide, deep to mid-purple to grey-lilac, rarely brown, dirty orange or yellow, often darkening rapidly on the opening of the inflorescence. *Staminodes* in 2 to 4 whorls forming a zone 2–10 mm long; bristles filiform, flexuous, 1.5–9 mm long, violet to deep purple; bases compressed conic, smooth, off-white. *Interstices*: upper and lower 0–2.5 mm long, usually with numerous rudimentary sterile flower bases, off-white. *Staminate flowers* in an oblong zone 3–25 mm long, 5–10 mm wide; anthers and connectives deep violet. *Pistillodes* in 2 or 3 or rarely 4 whorls; bristles filiform, flexuous, 1.5–9 mm long, violet to deep purple; bases compressed conic, smooth, off-white. *Pistillate flowers* in an oblong cluster 7–25 mm long, 5–17 mm wide; ovaries oblong-ovoid, 2–2.5 mm long, somewhat truncate apically, pale to mid-green, often stained with purple apically (this feature differing even within the same population); stigma purplish grey. *Fruiting spike* oblong-cylindric, 3–6 cm long, 1.5–2.5 cm wide when mature; berries ovoid, 5–11 mm long, 2–5 mm wide. *Germination* unknown.

Key to the Varieties

1. Spathe-limb interior deep purple or maroon, very rarely mid-brown; spadix-appendix deep to mid-purple, rarely brown, dirty orange or yellow **a. var. rupicola**
   Spathe-limb interior pale greenish white, often with a narrow purple border; spadix-appendix grey-lilac **b. var. virescens**

a. var. rupicola
?*A. kotschyi* Boiss. & Hohen. in Boiss., Diagn. 1 (13): 8 (1853). Type: Iran; in Dudera montis Elburs, Persia borealis, 1843, *Kotschy* 725 (holotype G! isotype P!).
A. ehrenbergii Schott in Oesterr. Bot. Zeit. 8: 386 (1858). Type: Syria (holotype W, destroyed; lectotype selected here: Schott Icones Aroideae no. 1439, W!).
A. detruncatum C.A. Meyer ex Schott, Prodr. Syst. Aroid., 80 (1860). Type: Azerbaijan, in rupestris as Schahbulagh, 13 May 1819, *Szovits* 147 (holotype LE! isotype G!).

referable to *A. rupicola sensu stricto*; **D**, spadix, from clone referable to *A. detruncatum sensu stricto*; **E**, base of spadix, from clone referable to *A. detruncatum sensu stricto*; **F**, spadix, from clone referable to *A. conophalloides sensu stricto*; **G**, base of spadix, from clone referable to *A. conophalloides sensu stricto*.

A. conophalloides Kotschy ex Schott, *op. cit* 97. Type: Turkey, Cataonia, Gorumse in devexis versus Sarum flumen, 14 May 1859, *Kotschy* 81 (holotype W, destroyed; isotypes BM! G! K!).

A. rupicola Boiss. var. *conophalloides* (Kotschy ex Schott) Engler in A. & C. DC., Monogr. Phan. 2: 588 (1879).

A. detruncatum C.A. Meyer ex Schott var. *conophalloides* (Schott ex Kotschy) Boiss., Fl. Orient. 5: 36 (1882).

A. hygrophilum Boiss. var. *rupicola* (Boiss.) Boiss., *op. cit.* 38.

A. engleri Hausskn. in Mitt. Geog. Ges. (Thur.) Jena 9: 22 (1890). Type: Iran, Mt. Raswend, prope Abbasabad, *Stauss* 371 (holotype WU!).

A. elongatum Steven forma *detruncatum* (C.A. Meyer ex Schott) Hruby in Bull. Soc. Bot. Genève 4: 145 (1912).

A. elongatum Steven forma *engleri* (Hausskn.) Hruby, *loc. cit.*

A. conophalloides Kotschy ex Schott var. *typicum* Engler, Pflanzenr. 73 (IV. 23F): 75 (1920). Type: as for *A. conophalloides* Kotschy ex Schott.

A. conophalloides Kotschy ex Schott var. *typicum* Engler subvar. *purpureum* Engler, *op. cit.*, 76. Type: Turkey, Phrygia, in regione subalpina montis Sultandagh prope Akscheher (Wilajet Konia), 1 July 1899, *Bornmüller* 5569 (B!). (Lectotype selected here. This specimen is by far the best preserved of the syntypes at Berlin and thus the logical lectotype.)

A. conophalloides Kotschy ex Schott var. *caudatum* Engler. *op. cit.*, 76. Type: Turkey; Kurdistan, Mardin, an Bächen bei Khanaki, 29 May 1888, *Sintenis* 1218 (lectotype selected by Mill (1984), B, destroyed; isolectotypes E! LD; WU).

A. orientale Bieb. subsp. *engleri* (Hausskn.) Engler, *op. cit.*, 80.

A. orientale Bieb. subsp. *detruncatum* (C.A. Meyer ex Schott) Engler, *op. cit.*, 81.

A. elongatum Steven subsp. *detruncatum* (C.A. Meyer ex Schott) H. Riedl in Rechinger, Fl. Iranica 1: 5 (1963).

A. elongatum Steven subsp. *engleri* (Hausskn.) H. Riedl in Rechinger, *loc. cit.*

? *A. giganteum* Ghahreman in Iran. Journ. Bot. 2: 80 (1983). Type: Iran, between Islamabad-e Gharb and Ilam, 63 km to Ilam, montane forest of *Quercus, Ghahreman* 2558 (holotype TARI).

A. detruncatum C.A. Meyer ex Schott var. *caudatum* (Engler) K. Alpinar & R. Mill in Davis, Fl. Turkey 10: 220 (1988). Type: as for *A. conophalloides* Kotschy ex Schott var. *caudatum* Engler.

DESCRIPTION. As in key.

ILLUSTRATIONS. PLATE 9. The plant illustrated is referable to *A. cono-phalloides*. Riedl in Townsend & Guest, Flora of Iraq 8: 191, pl. 50 (1985); Phillips & Rix, Bulbs, 119 (1989) as *A. conophalloides* var. *syriacum*.

FLOWERING PERIOD. Early May to late June, often flowering into July in cultivation.

HABITAT. Rocky hillsides, amongst *Quercus* scrub, margins of *Cedrus* forest, open montane pasture; 600–1,700 m.

DISTRIBUTION. Greece (Lesbos), Turkey, Iraq, Iran, Syria, Lebanon, Israel, Jordan, Cyprus, Belorussia. MAP 16a, p. 136.

b. var. **virescens** (Stapf) Boyce, **comb. nov.**

A. virescens Stapf in Denkschr. Akad. Wiss. Wien, Math.-Nat. Kl. 50: 6 (1855). Type: Iran, inter Kudrun et Rudbar, 22 April 1882, *Pichler* s.n. (holotype W!).

A. elongatum Steven forma *virescens* (Stapf) Hruby in Bull. Soc. Bot. Genève 4: 145 (1912).

A. conophalloides Kotschy ex Schott var. *typicum* Engler subvar. *virescens* (Stapf) Engler, Pflanzenr. 73 (IV. 23F): 75 (1920).

A. conophalloides Kotschy ex Schott var. *virescens* (Stapf) Bornm. & Gauba in Feddes Rep. Sp. Nov. 47: 71 (1939).

A. detruncatum C.A. Meyer ex Schott var. *virescens* (Stapf) K. Alpinar & R. Mill in Davis, Fl. Turkey 10: 220 (1988).

DESCRIPTION. As in key.

ILLUSTRATIONS. Gard. Chron. ser. 3, 115: 312 (1934); Phillips & Rix, Bulbs, 193 (1989).

FLOWERING PERIOD. April to June.

HABITAT. As for the typical variety.

DISTRIBUTION. Almost throughout the range of the species, but not yet gathered in Jordan, Cyprus or on Lesbos. MAP 16b, p. 136.

Var. *virescens* usually occurs as pure colonies in the midst of the typical variety but is never particularly abundant.

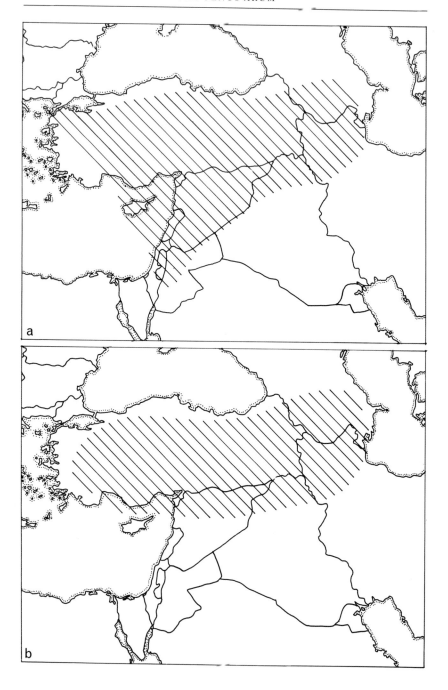

Map 16. Distribution of *Arum rupicola*. a: var. *rupicola*. b: var. *virescens*.

17. ARUM JACQUEMONTII

Although described in 1837, *A. jacquemontii* is hardly ever seen in cultivation although herbaria generally have no shortage of specimens, however, particularly from the 'North West Frontier'. *Arum jacquemontii* has a wide distribution, occurring from Iran through Afghanistan and northern India to China. It is the only *Arum* to occur in China (records of *A. korolkowii* in *Flora Republicae Popularis Sinicae* (Li, 1979) are referable to *A. jacquemontii*). The only living introductions I have been able to trace are those of Hewer from Afghanistan in 1971 and Grey-Wilson from Nepal in 1973.

Arum jacquemontii is an attractive species which should prove to be popular once it becomes more readily available. It is similar in appearance to both the widespread *A. rupicola* and the Central Asian *A. korolkowii*, and thus belongs to subsection *Tenuifila*, which is predominant in Asia Minor. Although similar to *A. korolkowii*, *A. jacquemontii* is readily distinguished by its dull purple, not striped, petioles, the purple spathe-limb, longer spadix-appendix and purple, not green, staminode and pistillode bases. Further, the pollen exine of *A. jacquemontii* is spinulose and not scabrose as in *A. korolkowii*. I have been unable to find any reference to the two species growing together in the same habitat. *Arum jacquemontii* grows further south and east, and at higher elevations than *A. korolkowii*. *Arum jacquemontii* is separable from *A. rupicola* primarily by the purple staminode and pistillode bases and the purple-stained petioles, although *A. jacquemontii* is generally smaller and more slender than *A. rupicola*.

With so little living material of this species available it would be inadvisable to generalize on its cultural requirements. The collections at Kew have been rather slow to reach flowering size, although it has otherwise proved to be an undemanding species. *Arum jacquemontii* would probably benefit from open ground treatment in the same way as many other members of the genus. With regard to hardiness, *A. jacquemontii* inhabits some of the coldest areas of western Asia, where severe winter weather is commonplace. On this basis it seems likely that there should be few problems with the species outdoors, except perhaps that it would need protection from excess winter wet.

Arum jacquemontii Blume, Rumphia 1: 118 (1836); Schott, Syn. Aroid., 13 (1856) & Prodr. Syst. Aroid., 99 (1860); Engler in A. & C. DC., Monogr. Phan. 2: 596 (1879) & in Engler, Pflanzenr. 73 (IV.

23F): 81 (1920). Type: Asia australis interior, *Jacquemonti* (holotype G! isotypes K! P!).

A. griffithii Schott, Syn. Aroid., 15 (1857). Type: Herb. Hooker (holotype K!).

DESCRIPTION. *Tuberous herb* sprouting in late autumn from a discoid, vertically orientated tuber 2–5 cm across, 2–2.5 cm thick. *Petiole* terete, 10.5–28 cm long, 2.5–4.4 mm wide, mid-green, ± stained with dull purple. *Leaf-blade* sagittate to sagittate-hastate, apex acute, 11–30 cm long, 4–12 cm wide, dark to mid-green. *Inflorescence* unscented. *Peduncle* exceeding the leaves, terete, 11–32 cm long, 5–7 mm wide, pale green below, deep green above. *Spathe* 12–22 cm long; spathe-tube oblong-cylindric, 2.5–4 cm long,

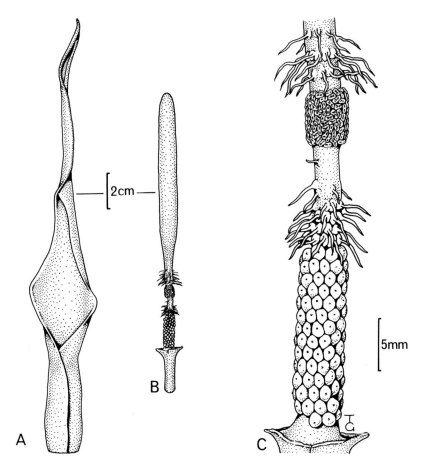

Arum jacquemontii. A, spathe; **B**, spadix; **C**, base of spadix.

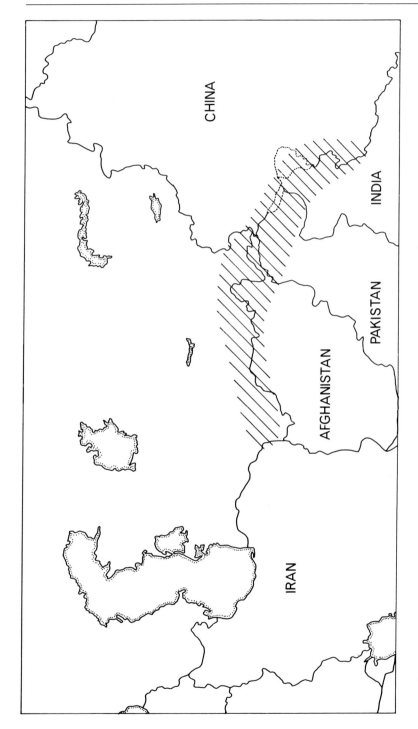

Map 17. Distribution of *Arum jacquemontii*.

1.2–1.6 cm wide, slightly constricted apically, exterior green, interior white; spathe-limb narrowly lanceolate, 9–18 cm long, 1–3 cm wide, erect at first but soon flopping forwards, acuminate, externally mid-green with faint purple staining, internally dull purple, deeper along the middle, brownish purple to purple apically, paler below. *Spadix c.* ⅔–¾ as long as the spathe-limb, 9–20 cm in total length; appendix cylindric, tapering basally, 6–17 cm long, 3–7 mm wide, dull yellow to orange-brown, purple or brownish purple, base paler. *Staminodes* in 2 or 3 whorls forming a zone 3–5 mm long; bristles filiform, flexuous, 2–2.5 mm long, glossy deep violet; bases barely conic, verrucate, dark purple. *Interstices*: upper 1.5–2 mm long, ± smooth, cream; lower 2.5–3 mm long, longitudinally ridged, cream. *Staminate flowers* in an oblong zone 6–7 mm long, 4–5 mm wide; anthers and connectives maroon. *Pistillodes* in 3 or 4 whorls forming a zone 3–4 mm long; bristles subulate-filiform, 3–4.5 mm long, glossy deep violet; bases bulbiform, verrucate, dark purple. *Pistillate flowers* in an oblong-cylindric cluster 15–17 mm long, 5–6 mm wide; ovaries oblong, 2–3 mm long, pale greenish yellow; stigma pale greyish mauve. *Fruiting spike* cylindric, 4–4.5 cm long, 1.8–2.2 cm wide; berries oblong, 4–9 mm long, 3–4 mm wide. *Germination* hypogeal.

ILLUSTRATIONS. PLATE 10. No others traced.

FLOWERING PERIOD. April to May.

HABITAT. Amongst rocks in damp soil pockets and crevices, occasionally along damp field edges; 1,600–3,650 m.

DISTRIBUTION. NE Iran, N Afghanistan, N Pakistan, N India, Nepal, W China. MAP 17, p. 139.

18. ARUM KOROLKOWII

Arum korolkowii is a rare and little known species which has only recently come into cultivation as a result of collections made in Soviet Central Asia during the early 1980s. An indication of the scarcity of this species in herbaria, let alone cultivation, can be gauged by the fact that as late as 1920 Engler listed it as a *species dubia*. *Arum korolkowii* was originally described by the German botanist Regel from material collected in Turkestan and grown on at the Botanic Gardens at St. Petersburg. The original description is brief but there can be no doubt that the plant Regel described is the same as that recently introduced.

Arum korolkowii is notable for its narrow, acuminate, mid-green spathe-limb, and brownish green striped petioles. Morphologically it is allied to *A. rupicola*, particularly the element of that species previously known as *A. detruncatum*, but the features noted above

140

under *A. rupicola*, together with their geographical disjunction, readily separates them. Within Central Asia *A. korolkowii* resembles *A. jacquemontii*, but differs in its green spathe-limb, cream staminodes and pistillode bases, and scabrose pollen.

In spite of having been in cultivation for only a short time, *A. korolkowii* has proved its worth as a garden plant. It is completely hardy, resisting not only winter cold but wet wintry conditions as well, and flowering reliably in April and May with the minimum of care.

Arum korolkowii Regel in Act. Hort. Petrop. 2: 407 (1877); Engler in A. & C. DC., Monogr. Phan. 2: 596 (1879) & in Engler, Pflanzenr. 73 (IV. 23F): 93 (1920). Type: Cult. in Hort. Petropolitana. Tubers collected by *Korolkov* s.n. in Central Asia (holotype LE!).

DESCRIPTION. *Tuberous herb* sprouting in early winter from a discoid, vertically orientated tuber 4–7 cm across, 2.5–3 cm thick. *Petiole* terete, 12–35 cm long, 4–5 mm wide, pale green with brownish green, rather diffuse longitudinal stripes. *Leaf-blade* sagittate-hastate to oblong-sagittate, apex acute to rather obtuse, 8–16 cm long, 5–13 cm wide, deep to mid-green. *Inflorescence* unscented. *Peduncle* exceeding the leaves, terete, 16–46 cm long, 5–7 mm wide, mid-green. *Spathe* 14–20 cm long; spathe-tube oblong-cylindric, 3–3.7 cm long, 1.5–2 cm wide, constricted apically, exterior mid-green, interior white; spathe-limb narrowly lanceolate, 11–17 cm long, 2.5–3 cm wide, erect, acuminate, externally mid-green, internally slightly paler with very faint purple flushing along the outer ⅓ of the limb. *Spadix c.* ⅔ as long as the spathe, 11–14 cm in total length; appendix cylindric-fusiform, shortly and stoutly stipitate, 8.8–10 cm long, 6–8 mm wide, dull cream, heavily marbled with reddish brown, darkening to purplish brown in the basal ⅓ stipe purple. *Staminodes* in 3 or 4 whorls, forming a zone 5–7 mm long; bristles filiform, flexuous, 3–4 mm long, pale purple; bases compressed-conic, verrucate, cream. *Interstices*: upper 1.5–2 mm long, verrucate, cream; lower 0–0.5 mm long, verrucate, with vestigal staminode bases, cream. *Staminate flowers* in a roughly quadratic zone 6–8 mm long, 5.5–7.5 mm wide; anthers and connectives mid-purple. *Pistillodes* in *c.* 4 whorls, forming a zone 3.5–4.5 mm long; bristles filiform, flexuous, 2.5–3.5 mm long, pale purple; bases bulbiform to conic, verrucate, cream. *Pistillate flowers* in an oblong-cylindric cluster 12–15 mm long, 7–9 mm wide; ovaries globose-oblong, 2.5–3 mm long, pale lime-green below, light green above; stigma cream. *Fruiting spike* oblong-cylindric, 5–6 cm long, 2–2.5 cm wide; berries oblong-pyriform, 5–10 mm long, 3–4.5 mm wide. *Germination* unknown.

ILLUSTRATIONS. Phillips & Rix, Bulbs, 119 (1989).

FLOWERING PERIOD. April to May.

141

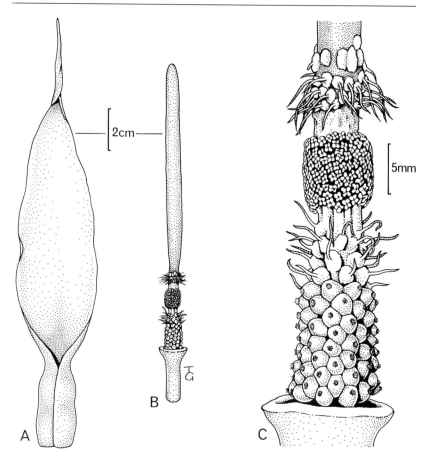

Arum korolkowii. **A**, spathe; **B**, spadix; **C**, base of spadix.

HABITAT. Soil pockets in rocky hillsides, beneath low scrub; 1,100–2,500 m.

DISTRIBUTION. N Iran, Afghanistan, Central Asia. MAP 18, p. 143.

d. Subsection Hygrophila

Arum subsection **Hygrophila** Boyce in Kew Bull. 44: 391 (1989). Type: *A. hygrophilum* Boiss.

Peduncles equal to or longer than petioles. *Spadix-appendix* sessile, less than 4 mm in diameter. *Staminodes and pistillodes* with long, filiform, flexuous bristles. *Spathe-tube* interior wholly purple. *Inflorescence* scentless.

142

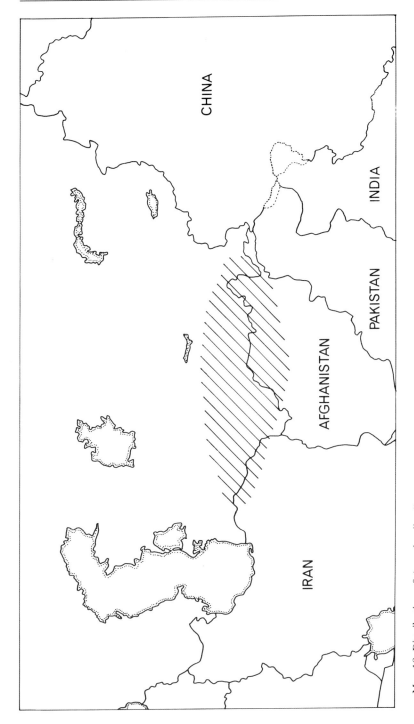

Map 18. Distribution of *Arum korolkowii*.

19. ARUM EUXINUM

The Black Sea coast of north-western Turkey, in particular the region around Abant Bölü, has yielded a number of attractive arums in the past few decades. Of these, *A. euxinum* is amongst the most interesting. Described by Robert Mill as recently as 1983, *A. euxinum* is related to *A. hygrophilum* by the peculiar waisted inflorescence, densely arranged staminodes, slender-cylindric, stalkless spadix-appendix and purple spathe-tube interior. This suite of characters is unique in the genus and led me to propose a separate subsection, subsect. *Hygrophila* (Boyce, 1989) for the two species. They also both have a preference for marshy places, an unusual habitat for arums.

   Arum euxinum has proved to be both easy to grow and hardy, but seems intolerant of summer heat. The best way to cultivate it under glass is in wide pans, each containing three to five tubers, and to ensure that the plants do not dry out completely in summer. Recent experience with *A. euxinum* suggests that it would make an interesting addition to a damp peat bed.

Arum euxinum R. Mill in Notes Roy. Bot. Gard. Edinb. 41: 46 (1983); Mill in Davis, Fl. Turkey 8: 48 (1984). Type: NW Turkey, Zonguldak: Kel Tepe, open meadow, somewhat marshy, 1450 m, 1 June 1967, *Tobey* 1837 (holotype E!).
[*A. incomptum* Schott, Prodr. Syst. Aroid., 88 (1860) *pro parte, excl. type*]
[*A. hygrophilum* Boiss. var. *ponticum* Hruby ex Bornm. in Bibl. Bot. Zentralb. 31 (2): 260 (1914).]
[*A. orientale* Bieb. subsp. *incomptum* (Schott) Engler, Pflanzenr. 73 (IV. 23F): 81 (1920) *pro parte, excl. type*]

DESCRIPTION. *Tuberous herb* sprouting in autumn from a discoid, vertically orientated tuber, 3–3.5 cm across, 1.5–2 cm thick. *Petiole* terete, 6–35 cm long, 2.5–4 mm wide, dark green suffused with purple, especially at the base. *Leaf-blade* oblong-hastate, apex acute to rather obtuse, 5–11 cm long, 2–6 cm wide, dark green. *Inflorescence* unscented. *Peduncle* exceeding the leaves, terete, 10.5–45 cm long, 3.5–5.5 mm wide, dark green, longitudinally striped and stained with purple. *Spathe* 8–14 cm long; spathe-tube ellipsoid-cylindric, 1.5–3 cm long, 1–1.5 cm wide, tapering apically, exterior pale green, stained with purple, especially along the margin and at the base, interior dark purple; spathe-limb ovate-lanceolate, 6.5–11 cm long, 1.5–4 cm wide, cucullate, acute to briefly acuminate, externally pale greenish stained with purple along the margin and at the base, internally greenish white with a broad, purple

Plate 13

Arum dioscoridis var. *dioscoridis*

PANDORA SELLARS

Plate 14

Arum palaestinum

PANDORA SELLARS

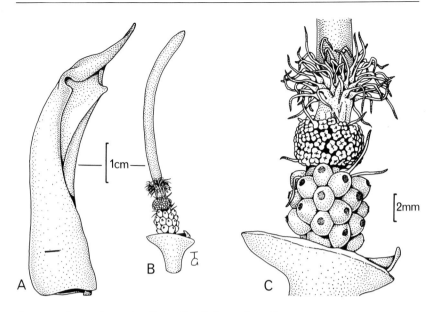

Arum euxinum. **A**, spathe; **B**, spadix; **C**, base of spadix.

margin. *Spadix* subequal to the spathe-limb, 4–7 cm in total length; appendix very slender-cylindric, stalkless, 2.5–4.5 cm long, 2.5–2.2 mm wide; dark purple. *Staminodes* in *c.* 4 whorls forming a zone 3–7 cm long; bristles filiform, flexuous, abundant, 2.5–5 mm long, cream with the upper ⅓ violet; bases barely conic, smooth, pale mauve. *Interstices*: upper 1–2 mm long, smooth, cream; lower 0–0.5 mm long, smooth, cream. *Staminate flowers* in a ± oblong zone 1.5–4 mm long, 2–3 mm wide; anthers and connectives violet. *Pistillodes* in 1 whorl forming a zone 0.7–3.7 mm long, sometimes absent; bristles filiform, flexuous, 2–4 mm long, cream, minutely tipped with violet; bases ± absent. *Pistillate flowers* in a cylindric cluster, 6–10 mm long; ovaries globose, 1.5–2 mm long, cream, with a very faint pale mauve ring around the stigma; stigma white. *Fruiting spike* cylindric, 3–4.5 (–7) cm long, 1.5–2 (–2.5) cm wide; berries oblong, 5–9 mm long, 2.5–3.5 mm wide. *Germination* unknown.

ILLUSTRATIONS. PLATE 11. No others traced.

FLOWERING PERIOD. Late May to June.

HABITAT. Open water meadow, between rocks, beneath *Juniperus* scrub; 300–1,680 m.

DISTRIBUTION. Black Sea coast of Turkey. MAP 19, p. 146.

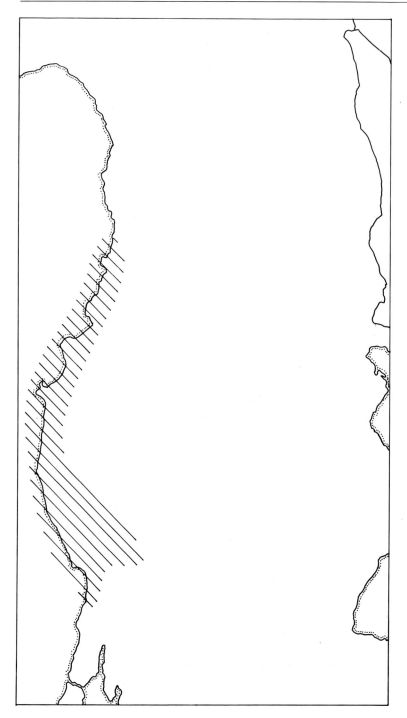

Map 19. Distribution of *Arum euxinum.*

20. ARUM HYGROPHILUM

Arum hygrophilum was originally collected from the area around Zabadani in Syria, very near the present Lebanese border, but is now known to occur in Israel, Cyprus, Lebanon and also far to the west in Morocco. It is an elegant and attractive plant which has the disadvantage of being one of the most tender species; indeed it is essential to have frost-free conditions in order for it to thrive. Once established it needs copious supplies of water, for the commonest natural habitat is along ditches and water-courses. It also needs heavy feeding, but is otherwise very easy to grow. *Arum hygrophilum* has one of the longest flowering periods of any *Arum* species, with the first spathes opening in late January and a large plant remaining in bloom until early June. A further horticultural bonus is the longevity of the individual inflorescences which, in cool weather, remain in good condition for up to two weeks.

Morphologically *A. hygrophilum* is distinct from the rest of the genus and has never fitted easily into the earlier sectional classifications. As discussed under the account of *A. euxinum*, the recognition of the latter species has done much to resolve the problem.

Throughout its range in the Middle East *A. hygrophilum* shows remarkably little variation in coloration and morphology. Occasionally a well-fed plant will attain particularly large dimensions, but the spathe does not show a corresponding increase in size. The major variation is found in plants of Northern African origin where the leaves have particularly long posterior lobes, the anterior lobe being relatively short and broad. The spadix-appendix is also rather shorter. This variant has been described as var. *maurum* (Br.-Bl. & Maire) Maire & Weiller. I have compared this variety with North African material of the typical variety and could find no reason to maintain their separation.

Arum hygrophilum Boiss., Diagn. 1 (13): 8 (1853); Schott, Syn. Aroid., 13 (1856) & Prodr. Syst. Aroid., 98 (1860); Engler in A. & C. DC., Monogr. Phan. 2: 589 (1879); Hruby in Bull. Soc. Bot. Genève 4: 157 (1912); Engler, Pflanzenr. 73 (IV. 23F): 77 (1920); Mayo & Meikle in Meikle, Fl. Cyprus 2: 1665 (1985). Type: Syria: ad fossae humidas et rivulos vallis Antilibani infra pagum Zebdani frequentissime, May 1846, *Boissier* s.n. (holotype G! isotype K!).
[*A. albinervium* Kotschy in mss. *nom. nud.*]

147

A. longicirrhum Schott, Syn. Aroid., 14 (1856). Type: Libanus (holo-type W, destroyed; lectotype selected here: Schott Icones Aroideae no. 1395, W!).

A. hygrophilum Boiss. var. *albinervium* Kotschy ex Engler in A. & C. DC., Monogr. Phan. 2: 590 (1879). Type: Turkey, Cilicia, montes Kassan Oghlu, inter Sis et Beilemhuj in jugo Hardun, *Kotschy* 441 (holotype B, destroyed).

A. hygrophilum Boiss. subsp. *maurum* Br.-Bl. & Maire in Bull. d'Hist. Nat. de L'Afrique 3, 1: 20 (1922). Type: Morocco, dans la vallée de l'Oued Mikès, 1888, *Grant* s.n. (holotype AL! isotype SIG-MA).

A. hygrophilum Boiss. var. *genuinum* Maire & Weiller in Maire, Fl. de l'Afrique du Nord 4: 236 (1957), *nom. illeg.*

A. hygrophilum Boiss. var. *maurum* (Br.-Bl. & Maire) Maire & Weiller, *op. cit.*, 232 (1957).

DESCRIPTION. *Tuberous herb* sprouting in early autumn from a discoid vertically (rarely horizontally) orientated tuber 3–6 cm across, 1.5–2.5 cm thick. *Petiole* terete, 9–75 cm long, 3–6 mm wide, bright mid-green, occasionally with purple staining along the sheath margin and at the petiole base. *Leaf-blade* lanceolate-hastate, apex acute to subacute, 8–45 cm long, 5–14 cm wide, dark to bright mid-green. *Inflorescence* unscented. *Peduncle* shorter than the leaves, terete, 15–45 cm long, 1.5–4 mm thick, bright mid-green. *Spathe* 7–14 cm long; spathe-tube ellipsoid, 2.5–3.8 cm long, 1.2–2.5 cm wide, waisted above, exterior pale to mid-green, occasionally with purple staining at the base and along the margin, rarely with the entire spathe-tube stained purple, interior deep purple, often with pale greenish white blotches on the rear wall near the base; spathe-limb oblong-lanceolate to elliptic-lanceolate, 5–11.5 cm long, 3–3.5 cm wide, erect to slightly cucullate, acuminate, externally pale to mid-green, purple-flushed along the margin, internally pale greenish white with a purple margin 0.5–1.5 mm wide. *Spadix* ⅔ as long as the spathe-limb, 7.5–9.5 cm in total length; appendix slender-cylindric, without a stipe, 5–7.5 cm long, 1.5–3 mm wide, deep purple, occasionally blotched apically with paler purple. *Staminodes* in 2 or 3 whorls, forming a zone 2–3.5 mm long; bristles filiform, flexuous, 4–5 mm long, pale cream, ± purple at the tip; bases conic, verrucate, cream, stained with purple. *Interstices*: upper 0–2 mm long, longitudinally ridged, cream; lower ± absent. *Staminate flowers* is a roughly quadratic zone 4–7 mm long, 5–6 mm wide; anthers and connectives reddish purple. *Pistillodes* in 2 or 3 whorls forming a zone 2–3 mm long; bristles filiform, flexuous, cream, stained with purple; bases bulbiform, minutely verrucate, cream, speckled with purple. *Pistillate flowers* in a cylindric cluster 4–10 mm long; ovaries oblong-fusiform, pale

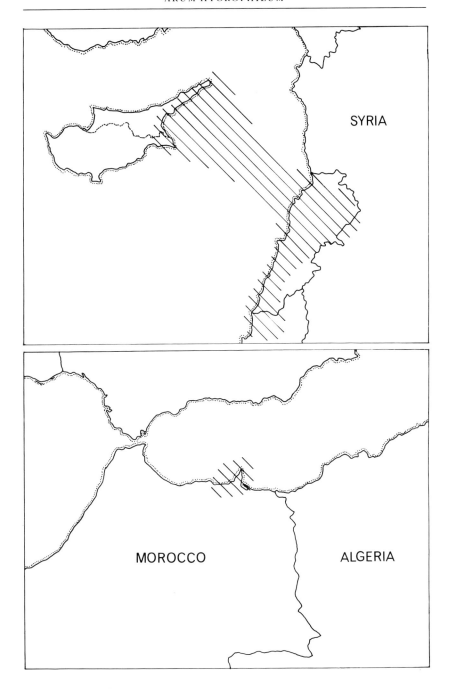

Map 20. Distribution of *Arum hygrophilum*.

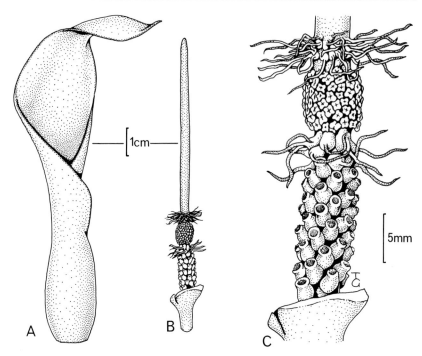

Arum hygrophilum. **A**, spathe; **B**, spadix; **C**, base of spadix.

lime-green with a faint purple ring around the stigma; stigma white. *Fruiting spike* oblong-cylindric, 4–6 cm long, 2–2.5 cm wide; berries angular-pyriform, 4–11 mm long, 3–5 mm wide. *Germination* epigeal.

ILLUSTRATIONS. PLATE 12. Nehmeh, Wild Fl. of Lebanon, pl.15 (1978).

FLOWERING PERIOD. February to May.

HABITAT. Stream-sides, ditches, wet flushes, damp soil pockets at rock bases; sea-level to 900 m.

DISTRIBUTION. Morocco, Cyprus, Syria, Lebanon, Israel, Jordan. MAP 20, p. 149 (note: map is in two parts).

e. Subsection Poeciloporphyrochiton

Arum subsection **Poeciloporphyrochiton** Schott, Prodr. Syst. Aroid., 74 (1860). Lectotype: *A. dioscoridis* Sm. (selected by Boyce in Kew Bull. 44: 391, 1989).

Arum subsection *Discotuberosae* Engler in A. & C. DC., Monogr. Phan. 2: 583 (1879). Lectotype: *A. dioscoridis* Sm. (selected by Boyce in Kew Bull. 44: 391, 1989).

150

Arum [infragen. group] *'Discotuberosae'* Engler in Engler & Prantl, Pflanzenfam. 2, 3: 147 (1889), rankless taxon (see Boyce, 1989).

Peduncles much shorter than petioles, sometimes apparently absent. *Spadix-appendix* shortly stipitate, cylindric to fusiform-cylindric or rather slender-cylindric, moderately stout. *Staminodes and pistillodes* well developed, bristles subulate, stiff, short to long. *Inflorescence* with foetid odour or smelling similar to fermenting apples, very rarely scentless.

21. ARUM DIOSCORIDIS

First gathered on Cyprus nearly 200 years ago, this spectacular species is deservedly popular with aroid fanciers due to its ease of culture. Most clones are hardy, free-flowering and have handsome coloration. There is one disadvantage in that, in flower, *A. dioscoridis* produces the strongest smell of any species in the genus, akin to a mixture of dung and rotting flesh. The typical plant has a spathe of the palest green with this colour almost obscured except towards the apex by maroon-purple blotches and staining. However, there is a wide range of variation in the markings; from unspotted pale green to almost pure purple. This colour variability has resulted in a large number of names being published and it requires some care to extricate the viable taxa from among them.

The way in which the variation has been approached differs from one botanist to another. The extreme viewpoints are those of Boissier (1853), who treated all the colour variations as the same taxon, and Schott (1860) who regarded them as all separate species. Boissier (1882) and Engler (1879; 1920) adopted several of Schott's names but at varietal and forma level. Koach (1986) followed Boissier (1853) in treating all the variation as belonging to one species. It was Engler's (1920) system that formed the basis for the latest partial treatment of *A. dioscoridis*, that of Mill (1983).

My observations have convinced me that some of these variations do in fact warrant varietal status. However, field-work in Turkey has failed to support the maintenance of two varieties recognized by Mill (1983), var. *liepoldtii* (Schott) Engler and var. *luschanii* R. Mill. In all the populations observed, these taxa intergraded fully with both each other and with Schott's var. *spectabile* (Schott, 1857a). Unfortunately,

151

the matter proved more complex when a problem became apparent with the nomenclature of these taxa. The type specimen of *A. dioscoridis*, an illustration in Sibthorp & Lindley's *Flora Graeca*, closely matches Schott's var. *spectabile*. Until now, var. *disocoridis* has been considered to be the plant with large, discrete spathe-blotches and little or no purple staining, Schott's var. *spectabile* being separated by its densely stained spathe with confluent blotches. However, the type illustration of *A. dioscoridis* clearly shows that var. *spectabile* is the same as var. *dioscoridis*. This means that the unstained, discretely blotched plant presently called var. *dioscoridis* requires another name. The next name available for this taxon is var. *cyprium* (Schott) Engler, and this is adopted here.

The name var. *philistaeum* has, in all the references to the genus consulted, been given the authority '(Kotschy ex Schott) Engler'. This is based on the combination published by Engler in *Das Pflanzenreich* (1920). However, the same combination was validly and effectively published in Boissier's *Flora Orientalis* (1882). Boissier's combination must therefore be used because of its priority.

Arum dioscoridis var. *syriacum* is recognized on the basis of the sparsely blotched spathe-limb coupled with the geographical separation from the remainder of the varieties.

Arum dioscoridis, together with *A. palaestinum*, comprises the subsection *Poeciloporphyrochiton*. This subsection has no obvious allies in the genus. The production of a strong smell, together with the subulate staminodes and pistillodes, is found in *A. nigrum*, in subsection *Dischroochiton*. *Arum nigrum* differs from *A. dioscoridis* by its clavate spadix, broader and relatively shorter, concolorous purple spathe-limb and distinctly bicoloured spathe-tube interior.

Arum dioscoridis Sm. in Sibthorp & Smith, Fl. Graec. Prodr. 2: 245 (1816); Schott, Syn. Aroid., 9 (1856) & Prodr. Syst. Aroid., 78 (1860); Engler in A. & C. DC., Monogr. Phan. 2: 583 (1879); Hruby in Bull. Bot. Soc. Genève 4: 153 (1912); Engler, Pflanzenr. 73 (IV. 23F): 72 (1920); Mayo & Meikle in Meikle, Fl. Cyprus 2: 1665 (1985). Type: Cyprus: in insulae Cypri cultis, inter segetes, vulgaris, *Sibthorp* s.n. (holotype: illustration in Sibthorp & Lindley, *Fl. Graeca* 10(1): t.947, 1840!).

DESCRIPTION. *Tuberous herb* sprouting in early autumn from a discoid, vertically orientated tuber, 5–10 cm across, 2.5–3 cm thick. *Petiole* terete, 13–50 cm long, 4–7 mm wide, mid-green, sometimes longitudinally striped with whitish green, more rarely stained with purple. *Leaf-blade* oblong-hastate to narrowly sagittate-hastate, apex acute, 13–45 cm long, 9–27 cm wide, mid-green, the main and secondary lateral veins sometimes conspicuously paler. *Inflorescence* smelling strongly of donkey-dung and carrion, rarely odourless. *Peduncle* usually much shorter than the leaves, rarely almost equalling the petioles, terete, 3.5–10(–42) cm long, 4–10 mm wide, mid-green, rarely stained with purple. *Spathe* 11–40 cm long; spathe-tube oblong-cylindric, 3–8 cm long, 2–3.5 cm wide, moderately constricted apically, exterior pale to mid-green, sometimes suffused with purple above and along the margin, interior ± greenish white, the apical portion sometimes stained with purple; spathe-limb lanceolate to lanceolate-elliptic, erect, acute to acuminate, 8–37 cm long, (2–)4–11 cm wide, externally pale to mid-green,

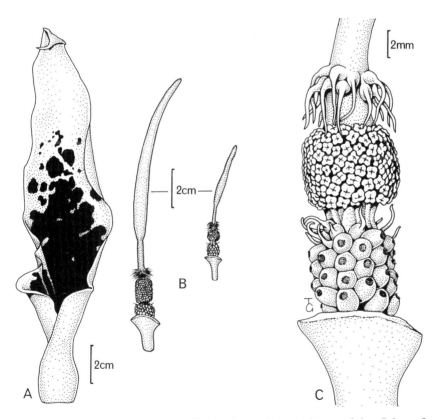

Arum dioscoridis. **A**, spathe; **B**, spadix, showing variation in shape and size; **C**, base of spadix.

occasionally stained with purple, especially towards the margin, internally greenish white to mid-green, variously blotched and stained with deep purple-maroon to black-purple, sometimes ± unspotted (var. *syriacum*) or ± uniformly purple (var. *philistaeum*). *Spadix* ½ as long to just exceeding the spathe-limb, 12–28 cm in total length; appendix stout-cylindric, fusiform cylindric or slender-cylindric, almost lacking a stipe to rather long-stipitate, 6–32 cm long, 3–12 mm wide, sooty purple to maroon-purple, very rarely dull yellow, stipe occasionally paler. *Staminodes* in 2 or 3 whorls forming a zone 1.5–8 mm long; bristles subulate to subulate-filiform, stiff, 2.5–9 mm long, cream to dull purple; bases bulbiform, verrucate, cream, sometimes stained with purple. *Interstices*: upper 0–5 mm long, longitudinally ridged, cream to dull yellow; lower 0–3 mm long, divided into ± diamond-shaped areas, cream to dull yellow. *Staminate flowers* in an oblong zone 2.5–8.5 mm long, 4.5–6 mm wide, anthers cream to cream with purple tips, connectives cream or purple. *Pistillodes* in (1–)2–5 whorls forming a zone 2.5–10 mm long; bristles subulate to subulate-filiform, stiff, 2–7 mm long, cream, to dull purple; bases compressed-bulbiform, verrucate, cream, sometimes stained with purple. *Pistillate flowers* in an oblong-cylindric cluster 8–30 mm long; ovaries oblong, somewhat truncate apically, pale green to pale yellow, stained with dark purple around the stigma; stigma pale lilac to dirty white. *Fruiting spike* stout-cylindric, 4–9 cm long, 2–3 cm wide; berries oblong-pyriform, 5–11 mm long, 4–6 mm wide. *Germination* epigeal.

Key to the Varieties

1. Spathe-limb stained with deep purple for at least ⅔ of its length ± uniformly purple, blotches ± confluent   2
   Spathe-limb ± pale green, unstained, with or without discrete to confluent blotches   3

2. Spathe-limb 16–37 cm long, basal ⅔ stained with purple, apical ⅓ pale green, unspotted; spadix-appendix stout, 8–12 mm wide
        a. var. **dioscoridis**
   Spathe-limb 8–14 cm long, ± uniformly purple; spadix-appendix slender, 3–4 mm wide   **d.** var. **philistaeum**

3. Spathe-limb with large discrete blotches, especially in the basal ⅓; spadix-appendix sooty purple   **b.** var. **cyprium**
   Spathe-limb with small, scattered blotches, not infrequently ± devoid of markings; spadix-appendix purple to dull yellow   **c.** var. **syriacum**

a. var. **dioscoridis**
A. spectabile Schott in Oesterr. Bot. Wochenbl. 7: 175 (1857). Type:

154

Turkey, in Tauro Ciliciae, *Kotschy* s.n. (holotype W, destroyed; lectotype selected here: Schott Icones Aroideae no. 1463, W!).

A. *liepoldtii* Schott, Prodr. Syst. Aroid., 77 (1860). Type: Turkey, Mersine, 1859, *Kotschy* s.n. (holotype W, destroyed; neotype, chosen by Mill in Davis, Fl. Turkey 8: 52 (1984): Turkey, Bulukli bei Mersina, *Balansa* 828 – E! isoneotypes BM! G! K!).

A. *dioscoridis* Sm. var. *smithii* Engler in A. & C. DC., Monogr. Phan. 2: 583 (1879). Type: as for A. *dioscoridis* Sm.

A. *dioscoridis* Sm. var. *spectabile* (Schott) Engler, *op. cit.*, 584.

A. *dioscoridis* Sm. var. *liepoldtii* (Schott) Engler, Pflanzenr. 73 (IV. 23F): 73 (1920).

A. *dioscoridis* Sm. var. *luschanii* R. Mill in Notes Roy. Bot. Gard. Edinb. 41: 46 (1983). Type: Turkey, Antalya?, Lycia, 1882, *Luschan* s.n., cult. Wien 1883 (holotype WU!).

DESCRIPTION. *Spathe-limb* 16–37 cm long, blotches ± confluent, basal ⅔ stained with purple, apical ⅓ pale green, unspotted. *Spadix-appendix* stout, 8–12 mm wide.

ILLUSTRATIONS. PLATE 13. Nehmeh, Wild Fl. of Lebanon, pl.13 (1978).

FLOWERING PERIOD. April to May.

HABITAT. Fallow fields, field margins, earth hillsides, waste places, uncultivated olive groves, often very abundant; sea-level to 2,500 m.

DISTRIBUTION. SW and central S Turkey, Cyprus. MAP 21a, p. 156.

b. var. cyprium (Schott) Engler, Pflanzenr. 73 (IV. 23F): 73 (1920).

A. *cyprium* Schott in Bonplandia 9: 368 (1861). Type: Cyprus, zwischen Larnaka und Oromidia, *Kotschy* 181 (holotype W, destroyed; isotype K!).

? A. *dioscoridis* Sm. forma *confluens* Hruby in Bull. Bot. Soc. Genève 4: 156 (1912). Type: not designated.

? A. *dioscoridis* Sm. forma *punctatum* Hruby, *loc. cit.* ('*punctata*').

? A. *dioscoridis* Sm. var. *punctatum* (Hruby) Engler, Pflanzenr. 73 (IV. 23F): 72 (1920).

[A. *dioscoridis* Sm. var. *dioscoridis* auct., *non* Sm.]

DESCRIPTION. *Spathe-limb* ± pale green, unstained, with large discrete blotches, especially in the basal ⅓. *Spadix-appendix* rather stout, 5–12 mm wide, sooty purple.

ILLUSTRATIONS. Phillips & Rix, Bulbs, 193 (1989) as A. *dioscoridis* var. *liepoldtii*.

FLOWERING PERIOD. April to May.

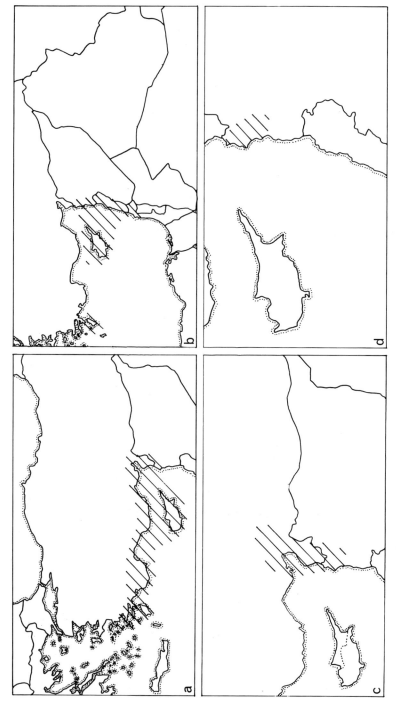

Map 21. Distribution of *Arum dioscoridis*. a: var. *dioscoridis*. b: var. *cyprium*. c: var. *syriacum*. d: var. *philistaeum*.

HABITAT. As for var. *dioscoridis*.

DISTRIBUTION. Islands of the E Aegean, Rhodes, Cyprus, Syria, Lebanon, Israel. MAP 21b, p. 156.

c. var. **syriacum** (Blume) Engler in A. & C. DC., Monogr. Phan. 2: 584 (1879) & in Engler, Pflanzenr. 73 (IV. 23F): 72 (1920).

A. syriacum Blume, Rumphia 1: 119 (1836). Type: Syria, *Labillardière* s.n. (holotype G!).

A. dioscoridis Sm. var. *syriacum* (Blume) Engler forma *guttatum* Engler in A. & C. DC., Monogr. Phan. 2: 584 (1879) ('*guttata*'). Type: Lebanon, Beirut, *Kotschy* 438 (holotype B, destroyed).

A. dioscoridis Sm. forma *guttatum* (Engler) Hruby in Bull. Soc. Bot. Genève 4: 156 (1912) ('*guttata*').

A. dioscoridis Sm. forma *viridulum* Hruby, *loc. cit.* ('*viridula*'). Type: not designated.

A. dioscoridis Sm. var. *viridulum* (Hruby) Engler, Pflanzenr. 73 (IV. 23F): 72 (1920).

DESCRIPTION. *Spathe-limb* ± pale green, unstained, with small, scattered blotches, not infrequently ± devoid of markings. *Spadix-appendix* purple to dull yellow.

ILLUSTRATIONS. Phillips & Rix, Bulbs, 119 (1989) as *A. dioscoridis* var. *spectabile*.

FLOWERING PERIOD. April to May.

HABITAT. As for var. *dioscoridis*.

DISTRIBUTION. Central S Turkey, NW Syria. MAP 21c, p. 156.

Several colonies of this taxon that I investigated in the southern Amanus Mountains of Turkey lacked the nauseous smell usually associated with *A. dioscoridis*. It is also interesting to note that albino forms of var. *syriacum*, which very closely resemble *A. italicum*, are not uncommon in south-east Turkey. Only when the tubers are seen is their true identity revealed.

d. var. **philistaeum** (Kotschy ex Schott) Boiss., Fl. Orient. 5: 39 (1882).

A. philistaeum Kotschy ex Schott, Prodr. Syst. Aroid., 79 (1860). Type: Syria, Palaestina, zwischen Gaza und Khan Junis, *Kotschy* 444 (holotype W, destroyed; lectotype selected here: Schott Icones Aroideae no. 1454, W!).

A. dioscoridis Sm. forma *atropurpureum* Hruby in Bull. Soc. Bot. Genève

4: 156 (1912) ('*atropurpurea*'). Type: not designated.
[*A. eggeri* Barbey in sched., *nom. nud.*]
[*A. pumilum* Kotschy in sched., *nom. nud.*]

DESCRIPTION. *Spathe-limb* 8–14 cm long, ± uniformly purple. *Spadix-appendix* slender, 3–4 mm wide.

ILLUSTRATIONS. None traced.

FLOWERING PERIOD. April to May.

HABITAT. As for var. *dioscoridis*.

DISTRIBUTION. NW Syria. MAP 21d, p. 156.

Little is known about this taxon except that, on the basis of the illustrations in the Naturhistorisches Museum, Vienna, it is definitely distinct from any other described in the Middle East. In several features, especially the robust pistillodes and staminodes and uniformly purple, though obscurely spotted, spathe-limb it is apparently intermediate between *A. dioscoridis* and *A. palaestinum*. That var. *philistaeum* could be a hybrid between the two species is not improbable, given the obvious closeness of the species and their geographical proximity, and requires further investigation.

22. ARUM PALAESTINUM

Arum palaestinum was originally collected by the Swiss botanist Boissier on Mount Carmel near Jerusalem. It is a very handsome species which, unfortunately, is not one of the easiest to maintain in good health since it seems prone to suffer from excess winter moisture. Additionally it really requires a sheltered position, ideally frost free, in order to thrive.

Arum palaestinum is allied to *A. dioscoridis*, both species sharing stiff, subulate sterile flowers, a relatively open spathe-tube, a moderately stout, shortly stipitate spadix-appendix and, usually, a strong odour when in blossom. They may be separated by the differences in inflorescence coloration (*A. palaestinum* has a purple spathe-limb with no trace of spotting), and by the thicker, shorter, sterile flowers found in *A. palaestinum*. Another important difference lies in the inflorescence odour. *Arum palaestinum* typically produces a smell similar to fermenting fruit, which is actually quite pleasant. On the other hand *A. dioscoridis* smells strongly of donkey-dung.

There appears, however, to be some variation in the odour produced by *A. palaestinum* when in flower. Mouterde (1966) reported that some Lebanese populations were scentless and Koach (1986) has reported an ecotype of *A. palaestinum* which smells weakly of dung and carrion. It is interesting that the typical ecotype occurs on terra-rossa derived from limestone and calcareous rocks, but the newly discovered ecotype grows on alluvial soils or on soils overlying sedimentary Eocene or basaltic rocks. Koach (1986) speculated that the overlapping of odour-type between *A. palaestinum* and *A. dioscoridis* might be due to introgression between the species.

Arum palaestinum Boiss., Diagn. 1 (13): 6 (1853); Schott, Syn. Aroid., 9 (1856) & Prodr. Syst. Aroid., 79 (1860); Engler in A. & C. DC., Monogr. Phan. 2: 585 (1879); Hruby in Bull. Bot. Soc. Genève 4: 156 (1912); Engler, Pflanzenr. 73 (IV. 23F): 76 (1920). Type: Israel, Hierosolyma (Jerusalem), in Monte Carmelo, *Boissier* s.n. (holotype G-BOIS!).

A. sanctum Dammann, Catal. 3: 3, t.1 (1889). Type: specimen not designated.

A. magdalenae Sprenger in Bull. Soc. Tosc. Ortic. 18: 277 (1894). Type: specimen not designated.

DESCRIPTION. *Tuberous herb* sprouting in autumn from a discoid, vertically, rarely horizontally, orientated tuber 4.5–8 cm across, 2–2.5 cm thick. *Petiole* terete, 15–21 cm long, 3–7 mm wide, dark to mid-green, often stained purple to *c.* ½-way up. *Leaf-blade* sagittate to oblong-sagittate, apex acute to subacute, 15–36 cm long, 10–25 cm wide, deep green. *Inflorescence* either smelling of fermenting apples or weakly of dung and carrion, rarely scentless. *Peduncle* shorter than to just exceeding the leaves, terete, 8–27.5 cm long, 4–6 mm wide, pale to mid-green, often stained purple for *c.* ⅔ of its length. *Spathe* 9–23 cm long; spathe-tube oblong-cylindric, 2.5–5 cm long, 1.5–3 cm wide, weakly constricted above, exterior greenish to pale brown, interior purple above, greenish white below; spathe-limb lanceolate, 6.5–23 cm long, 3.5–9 cm wide, erect on unfurling, ± reflexed at maturity, acuminate, externally pale green to pale greenish brown, with slight purple staining, internally deep uniform purple, the apex occasionally mid-green. *Spadix c.* ½ as long to subequal to the spathe-limb, 9.5–17 cm in total length; appendix fusiform-cylindric, obscurely stipitate, 7–19 cm long, 4–7 mm wide, black-purple. *Staminodes* in 1 or 2 whorls, forming a zone 1.5–3 mm long; bristles subulate, stiff, 9–11 mm long, deep purple; bases bulbiform, verruculose, purple. *Interstices*: upper 2–2.5 mm long, longitudinally ridged, purple; lower ±

159

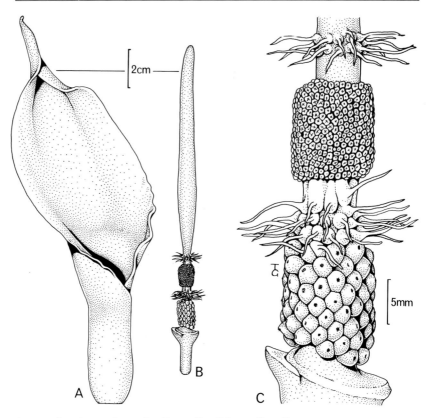

Arum palaestinum. **A**, spathe; **B**, spadix; **C**, base of spadix.

absent. *Staminate flowers* in a roughly oblong zone 9–13 mm long, 7–10 mm wide; anthers and connectives dark purple. *Pistillodes* in 2–5 whorls forming a zone 2.5–4 mm long; bristles subulate, stiff, 6–7 mm long, deep purple; bases bulbiform, verruculose, purple. *Pistillate flowers* in a cylindric cluster 11–14 mm long, 7–11 mm wide; ovaries oblong, 1.5–2 mm long, pale green stained with purple apically; stigma purple. *Fruiting spike* oblong-cylindric, 3–5 cm long, 2–3 cm wide; berries oblong, 4–11 mm long, 3.5–5 mm wide. *Germination* epigeal.

ILLUSTRATIONS. PLATE 14. Rix & Phillips, Bulbs, 192 (1989).

FLOWERING PERIOD. March to May.

HABITAT. Open hillsides, fallow fields, field margins, waste places. On limestone-derived terra-rossa and calcareous rocks, alluvial soils and soils derived from Eocene and basalt rocks; sea-level to 900 m.

DISTRIBUTION. Syria, Lebanon, Israel, ? Jordan (sterile material at K!).
MAP 22, p. 161.

Plate 15

Arum creticum × ⁵⁄₆

PANDORA SELLARS

Plate 16

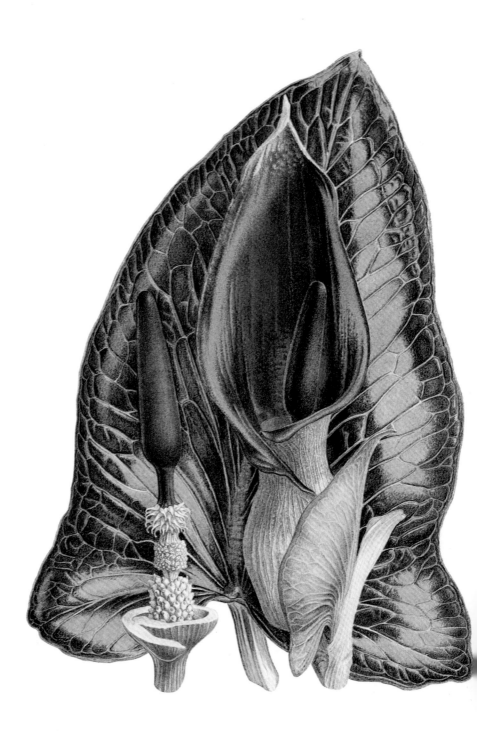

Arum pictum

PANDORA SELLARS

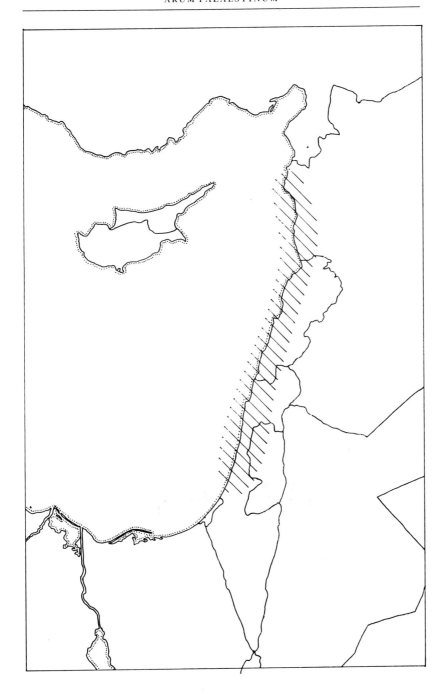

Map 22. Distribution of *Arum palaestinum*.

f. Subsection Cretica

Arum subsection **Cretica** (Engler) Boyce in Kew Bull. 44: 392 (1989).
Type: *A. creticum* Boiss. & Heldr.
Arum § *Cretica* Engler, Pflanzenr. 73 (IV. 23F): 68 (1920), rankless
taxon (see Boyce, 1989).

Peduncles longer, or much shorter, than petioles. *Spadix-appendix*
sessile to obscurely stipitate, cylindric, laterally compressed, moderately stout. *Staminodes and pistillodes* absent (very rarely present in *A.*
creticum). *Inflorescence* sweetly scented or scentless.

23. ARUM IDAEUM

Arum idaeum has often been confused with *A. creticum* perhaps because
in the dried state *A. idaeum* and *A. creticum* are virtually indistinguish-
able, although in living material the differences are clear. In *A. idaeum*
the unscented inflorescence is carried beneath the leaves, and has an
erect, cucullate, white spathe-limb. The spadix is usually deep purple
as are the staminate flowers, while the ovaries are lime-green. This is
in sharp contrast to *A. creticum* in which the strongly scented inflorescences are held above the leaves with the creamy yellow spathe-limb
reflexed to reveal a yellow spadix-appendix with yellow staminate
flowers and whitish green ovaries.

Greuter (1984) showed that the two species had been confused in
descriptions of *A. creticum*, which gave the impression of great
variability in the latter. This 'variation' was often accounted for by
reference to the existence of high and low altitude forms of *A.*
creticum, but Greuter's work established that two species were involved.

Arum idaeum is closely allied to *A. creticum* by the absence of sterile
flowers, a laterally flattened spadix-appendix, the somewhat pyramid-
al arrangement of the pistillate flowers and in having the spathe-tube
interior unmarked in any way. The robust nature of the spadix-
appendix and rather wide spathe-tube entrance are both features
shared with *A. palaestinum*. Although morphologically *A. idaeum* and
A. creticum are clearly distinct, plants occur which are intermediate in
colour. In particular forms of *A. idaeum* exist with yellow and

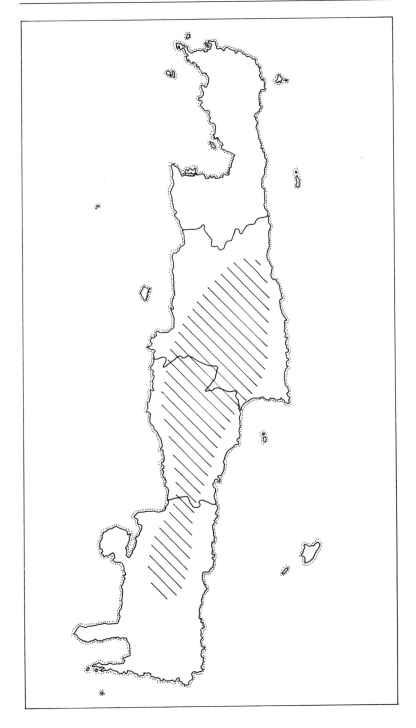

Map 23. Distribution of *Arum idaeum*.

purple-and-yellow marbled spadix-appendices. Whether these individuals represent hybrids between the two species is still unclear. As yet material typical of *A. creticum* but with influences of *A. idaeum* have not been found.

Arum idaeum inhabits rocky slopes high in the mountains of central and southern Crete. *Arum creticum*, which generally flowers earlier, occurs at lower altitudes, on plateaus, between boulders and on grassy slopes. In cultivation *A. idaeum* has shown itself to be very hardy, surviving the most severe weather unscathed. In fact it is seldom happy under glass and if cultivated in this way requires ample ventilation and moisture.

Arum idaeum Coust. & Gandoger in Bull. Soc. Bot. Fr. 63: 11 (1917). Type: Crete, montis Ida ad nives, alt. 6,500 ft., 5 July 1914, *Gandoger* 5471 (lectotype selected by Greuter (1984) LY; isolectotypes FI! K!).

DESCRIPTION. *Tuberous herb* sprouting in early winter from a discoid, horizontally orientated tuber 3.5–5 cm across, 1.5–2.5 cm thick. *Petiole* terete, 8–21 cm long, 6–7 mm wide, dark green, heavily stained with purple, especially at the base. *Leaf-blade* oblong-sagittate, apex bluntly acute, 10–22.5 cm long, 8–17 cm wide, deep green. *Inflorescence* unscented. *Peduncle* shorter than to just equalling the leaves, terete, 5–17 cm long, 3.5–5 mm wide, deep green, heavily stained with deep purple, the staining ending abruptly at the base of the spathe-tube. *Spathe* 7.5–11 cm long; spathe-tube broadly oblong-cylindric, 2.5–4 cm long, 1.5–2.5 cm wide, slightly constricted apically, exterior pale lime-green with very faint purple marbling basally, margin whitish green, interior whitish green; spathe-limb narrowly elliptic to lanceolate, 5–9 cm long, 2.5–3.5 cm wide, erect, cucullate, acute, externally white tinged with pale green, internally white with numerous scattered translucent patches, margin with a very narrow purple border. *Spadix c.* ¾ as long as the spathe-limb, 7.5–9.5 cm in total length; appendix fusiform-cylindric, laterally compressed, shortly and stoutly stipitate, 5.5–7 cm long, 6–9 mm wide, dull deep purple with a few lilac patches, rarely dirty yellow with diffuse pale purple marbling, stipe encircled by a narrow lilac band basally, rarely dirty cream. *Staminodes* and *pistillodes* absent, but very rarely a few vestigial purple staminodes may be present. *Interstices* absent. *Staminate flowers* in a conical zone 7–9 mm long, 6–7 mm wide, contiguous with the pistillate flowers; anthers and connectives deep purple. *Pistillate flowers* in an oblong-cylindric cluster 14–17 mm long, 9–12 mm wide; ovaries oblong, rounded apically, lime-green; stigma white. *Fruiting spike* oblong-cylindric, 3.5–6 cm long, 2–2.5 cm wide; berries oblong-pyriform, 5–9 mm long, 3.5–5 mm wide. *Germination* hypogeal.

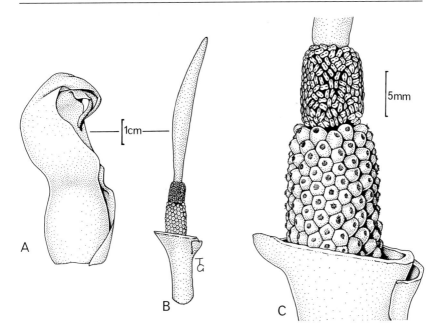

Arum idaeum. **A**, spathe; **B**, spadix; **C**, base of spadix.

ILLUSTRATIONS. Huxley & Taylor, Flowers of Greece and the Aegean, f.418 (1977) as *A. creticum*.

FLOWERING PERIOD. May to June.

HABITAT. Soil pockets between boulders, scree, stony mountain meadows, often close to the snow-line; 600–1,750 m.

DISTRIBUTION. Greece (Crete). MAP 23, p. 163.

24. ARUM CRETICUM

Possibly the most popular member of the genus, *A. creticum* is a lovely addition to a partially heated glasshouse or a sunny, sheltered border. Originally described by Boissier (1853) from material collected on Crete, the plant seems to have been in continuous cultivation ever since and, with its powerfully fragrant yellow inflorescences, it is one of the most distinctive species of *Arum*.

For many years *A. creticum* was thought to be restricted to the island of Crete, but it has also been collected on Karpathos, and more recently on the Turkish mainland (Baytop, 1982). Its distribution is very similar to that of *Biarum davisii*, also thought at one time to be

165

restricted to Crete. However, it should be noted that the Turkish plants of *B. davisii* constitute a separate subspecies (subsp. *marmarisense* Boyce, 1987b) while the Turkish plants of *A. creticum*, although differing from the Cretan plants in certain respects, are insufficiently distinct to warrant formal taxonomic recognition. The long-standing confusion with *A. idaeum* has been dealt with previously.

The spathe coloration and the sweet inflorescence odour suggest an adaptation to a pollinator different from the flies, midges or beetles usually associated with *Arum*. Pleasant scents, however, occur also in *A. gratum* and *A. palestinum*, both with darker coloured inflorescences. Other characters that are probably also related to pollination biology are the absence of staminodes and pistillodes and the noticeably less constricted spathe-tube. *Arum idaeum*, which also lacks staminodes and pistillodes, still possesses a constricted spathe-tube and perhaps can be interpreted as intermediate between subsection *Cretica* and the remainder of *Arum*.

The typical habitat of the species is in garrigue or on grassy, rocky mountain sides but it can also be found on the plateau areas growing in stony terra-rossa often among *Euphorbia acanthothamnos*. The relatively high altitude of these sites suggests that the species is quite hardy. However, this is not always the case and care should be taken when first cultivating *A. creticum* to determine the hardiness of the particular clone being grown. The form that received a First Class Certificate from the Royal Horticultural Society in 1976 (see *Bull. Alpine Gard. Soc.* 44: 266, 1976) is particularly reliable. Frost hardiness of the Turkish plants is as yet unknown.

Arum creticum Boiss. & Heldr. in Boiss., Diagn. 1 (13): 9 (1853); Schott, Syn. Aroid., 11 (1856) & Prodr. Syst. Aroid., 94 (1860); Engler in A. & C. DC., Monog. Phanerog. 2: 590 (1879); Hruby in Bull. Soc. Bot. Genève 4: 151 (1912); Engler, Pflanzenr. 73 (IV. 23F): 69 (1920). Type: Crete, sommet du mont Afendis, Sitia, 27 April 1846, *Heldreich* 1407 (lectotype selected by Greuter (1984) G-BOIS!).

DESCRIPTION. *Tuberous herb* sprouting in early autumn from a discoid, vertically orientated tuber 4–6.5 cm across, 2–3 cm thick. *Petiole* 10–35 cm long, 4–7 mm wide, terete, bright mid-green, rarely dull purple for ± its whole length. *Leaf-blade* sagittate to oblong-sagittate, or oblong-sagittate-hastate, apex acute to obtuse, 8–27 cm long, 4–18.5 cm wide, bright mid-green. *Inflorescence* smelling strongly of freesia and lemon with a slightly

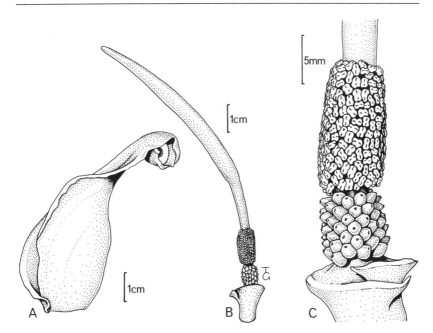

Arum creticum. **A**, spathe; **B**, spadix; **C**, base of spadix.

sour overtone, reminiscent of naphtha at close quarters. *Peduncle* equal to or exceeding the leaves, terete, 12–30 cm long, 4–6 mm wide, bright mid-green, rarely deep purple. *Spathe* 4.5–24 cm long; spathe-tube goblet-shaped, 1.5–4 cm long, 1–3.5 cm wide, flaring apically, exterior pale to mid-yellow, with slight green staining at the base, interior pale yellow, generally paler than the exterior; spathe-limb lanceolate, 2.5–20 cm long, 1–5.5 cm wide, becoming reflexed and ± twisted at maturity, acuminate, externally and internally pale to mid-yellow, sometimes pale creamy white. *Spadix* equalling to just exceeding the spathe, 3.5–16.5 cm in total length; appendix fusiform-cylindric, laterally compressed, indistinctly stipitate, 2.5–11.5 cm long, 2–9 mm wide, deep to mid-yellow, stipe generally paler, appendix generally darker than the spathe-limb. *Staminodes* and *pistillodes* usually absent but occasionally small, subulate yellow staminodes and vestigial pistillodes may be present. *Interstices*: upper absent; lower 0–3.5 mm long, longitudinally ridged, pale yellow. *Staminate flowers* in a roughly conical zone 4–18 mm long, 2–4 mm wide, sometimes ± contiguous with the pistillate zone; anthers and connectives yellow. *Pistillate flowers* in a cylindric cluster 5–20 mm long, ovaries ovoid, 2–2.5 mm long, whitish green; stigma cream. *Fruiting spike* oblong-cylindric, 5–7 cm long, 2–2.5 cm wide; berries oblong, 5–11 mm long, 3–5 mm wide. *Germination* epigeal.

ILLUSTRATIONS. PLATE 15. Phillips & Rix, Bulbs, 178 (1989).

167

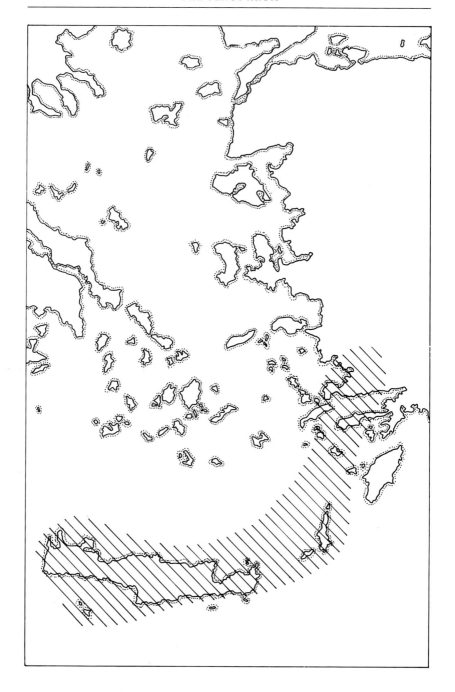

Map 24. Distribution of *Arum creticum*.

FLOWERING PERIOD. March to May.

HABITAT. Garrigue, rocky grassy hillsides, open meadows amongst low scrub; 250–1,500 m.

DISTRIBUTION. Greece (Crete, Karpathos, Kasos), SW Turkey. MAP 24, p. 168.

2. Subgenus Gymnomesium

Arum subgenus **Gymnomesium** (Schott) Engler in Engler & Prantl, Pflanzenfam. 2, 3: 147 (1889).

Gymnomesium Schott in Oesterr. Bot. Wochenbl. 5: 17 (1855). Type: *G. pictum* (L. fil.) Schott.

Arum section *Gymnomesium* (Schott) Engler in A. & C. DC., Mongr. Phan. 2: 581 (1879).

Arum § *Gymnomesium* Engler, Pflanzenr. 73 (IV. 23F): 68 (1920), rankless taxon (see Boyce, 1989).

Description as in the key to the subgenera (p. 56).

25. ARUM PICTUM

For many, the primary attraction of the genus *Arum* is the unique structure of the inflorescence coupled with its often rich coloration. Only occasionally is the foliage mentioned as a further source of interest. *Arum pictum* is one of the two notable exceptions, the other being *A. italicum* subsp. *italicum*. The leaves of *A. pictum* display a variety of colours, depending on their stage of development. On first emerging they are deep, shiny, metallic green, with the margins, and to a certain extent the blade, tinged with purple. As the leaf expands the purple blade coloration fades while the main and lateral veins become slightly paler. However, the margin retains its coloration. As the season progresses the blade loses its sheen but the veins continue to lighten until late spring, when they stand out as a creamy white to silvery grey network. The late season colour of the leaves of *A. pictum* is similar to that of many forms of *A. italicum* subsp. *italicum* with silvery grey veining, although the leaf shape is very different. In view

169

of this similarity it is hardly surprising that these two plants have been confused in the past despite their different growth habit and appearance.

Arum pictum produces inflorescences at the start of the growth period in the autumn, a unique flowering pattern in the genus. In flower *A. pictum* resembles *A. nigrum*, except that the peduncle is far shorter and the spathe-limb has a much more pronounced sheen. Close inspection of the spadix reveals only a single zone of sterile flowers, the staminodes, situated above the staminate flowers. Furthermore the inflorescence of *A. nigrum* is produced from the petiole-sheath of the terminal leaf at the completion of the growth period, usually in April or May, whereas in *A. pictum* the inflorescence emerges just before, or with, the leaves at the start of the growth period.

Arum pictum was described by the younger Linnaeus; later Schott (1855) transferred it to a new genus, *Gymnomesium*, justifying the separation on the presence of a single, upper zone of sterile flowers together with autumn flowering. However, *Gymnomesium* was not widely accepted and many botanists still retained the species within *Arum*. Engler (1879) at first treated *Gymnomesium* as a section within *Arum* but in *Die Natürlichen Pflanzenfamilien* (1889) raised it to subgeneric rank. However, in *Das Pflanzenreich*, Engler (1920) once again treated *Gymnomesium* as a 'section', assigning it an ambigous rank (see Boyce, 1989). Following Engler (1889) I have adopted subgeneric rank for this taxon in order to emphasize the singularity of *A. pictum*.

Arum pictum is easily grown in a large pot, or in warm areas outdoors in a sunny, well-drained position. Its hardiness has been doubted by many .growers, but a large clump of this species grown outdoors at the Cambridge Botanic Garden has survived many winters with minimal damage.

Arum pictum L. fil., Suppl., 410 (1782); Engler in A. & C. DC., Monogr. Phan. 2: 582 (1879); Hruby in Bull. Soc. Bot. Genève 4: 158 (1912); Engler, Pflanzenr. 73 (IV. 23F): 69–70 (1920). Type: probably described from cultivated material at Uppsala. (Lectotype designated here: Herb. Linn. 1079.9 [LINN !].) There is no material of *A. pictum* attributable to either Linnaeus or Linnaeus filius in Uppsala. The single specimen in the Herbarium of the Linnean Society of London, is in excellent condition and is the best candidate for the lectotype.

170

A. balearicum Buc'hoz. Stated to have been published in Hist. Univ. 8: t.2 (1775) but the validation does not appear anywhere in this work and I have been unable to trace any other place of publication. Type: the type would, presumably, be the illustration cited above since Buc'hoz's herbarium is not known to exist. In Leiden Herbarium there is an illustration corresponding to the missing one.

Gymnomesium pictum (L. fil.) Schott in Oesterr. Bot. Wochenbl. 5: 17 (1855), Schott, Syn. Aroid., 8 (1856); Schott, Prodr. Syst. Aroid., 73 (1860). Type: as for *A. pictum* L. fil.

Arum pictum L. fil., lusus (sport) *bispathaceum* Engler, Pflanzenr. 73 (IV. 23F): 72 (1920). Type: this plant was sent to the editors of *Gardeners' Chronicle* by Sprenger in 1904 (*Gard. Chron.* 36: 304, 1904). There is no material present in Berlin. Engler (1920) states 'von Herrn Sprenger in kultur beobachtet', quotes *Gardeners' Chronicle* reference, but does not refer to any specimens. From this I think it can be assumed that the type never existed.

A. corsicum Loisel., Fl. Gall. (edn. 1) 2: 617 (1807). Type: not designated.

DESCRIPTION. *Tuberous herb* sprouting in early to mid-autumn from a discoid vertical tuber 5–7 cm across, 2–2.5 cm thick. *Petiole* semiterete, 15–25 cm long, 2–12 mm wide, pale to mid-green with slight purple staining basally, with a conspicuous, open. triangular basal sheath. *Leaf-blade* ovate-cordate, apex acute to obtuse, 9–25 cm long, 6–18 cm wide, shiny, deep metallic green tinged with purple, especially along the margins when first expanded, the veins paler, blade later becoming dull, deep green with a purple tinge and creamy white to silvery grey main and lateral veins, leaves very occasionally plain green. *Inflorescence* appearing before or with the leaves, smelling strongly of horse-dung. *Peduncle* sessile at ground level, or rarely with up to 2 cm visible if growing in deep shade, terete, pale green. *Spathe* 11.5–21.5 cm long; spathe-tube oblong-cylindric, 2.5–5.5 cm long, 2.5–3 cm wide, constricted at the apex, exterior off-white below ground, pale green with scattered purple spots and staining above ground, interior dirty white with purple staining along the margins; spathe-limb elliptic, 9–16 cm long, 4–6.5 (–8) cm wide, slightly cucullate, shortly acuminate, externally mid-green with heavy, deep purple staining, especially along the margins at the apex, internally velvety deep purple, the apex occasionally mottled mid-green. *Spadix* approximately ⅗ as long as spathe-limb, 8–13 cm in total length; appendix stoutly clavate, cylindric, long-stipitate, 6–11 cm long, 7–15 mm

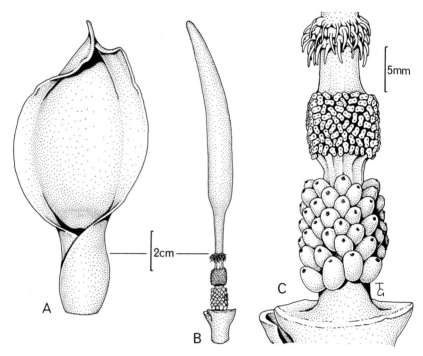

Arum pictum. **A**, spathe; **B**, spadix; **C**, base of spadix.

wide, deep purple-black with a satin sheen. *Staminodes* in 3 whorls forming a zone 3–5 mm long; bristles subulate, stiff, 3–4.5 mm long, cream; bases slightly swollen, smooth, cream. *Interstices*: upper 2–3 mm long, longitudinally ridged, off-white; lower 1–2 mm long, longitudinally deeply sulcate, cream. *Staminate flowers* in an oblong to globose zone 5–7 mm long and wide; anthers pale cream and connectives off-white. *Pistillodes* absent or very rarely a few vestigial bases present above the pistillate flowers. *Pistillate flowers* in a globose-cylindric cluster 11–13 cm long, 10–11 mm wide; ovaries oblong, tapering basally, 2.5–3 mm long, pale cream; stigma yellow. *Fruiting spike* elongate-globose, 2.5–5 cm long, 2–4 cm wide; berries oblong-globose, 5–11 mm long, 5–7 mm wide. *Germination* epigeal.

ILLUSTRATIONS. PLATE 16. Grey-Wilson & Mathew, Bulbs, pl.35 (1981).

FLOWERING PERIOD. October.

HABITAT. In garrigue and *Pinus halepensis* maquis; sea-level to 500 m.

DISTRIBUTION. Balearic Islands (Majorca, Minorca), Corsica, Sardinia, W Central Italy (Tuscany) MAP 25, p. 173.

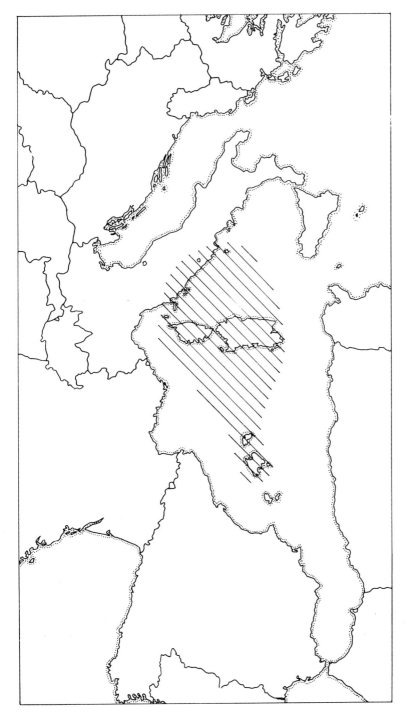

Map 25. Distribution of *Arum pictum*.

INCOMPLETELY KNOWN
AND DOUBTFUL SPECIES

The names below refer to poorly known or doubtful taxa. In most cases this is due to a complete lack of herbarium material, particularly with regard to some of Schott's names for which almost all material was destroyed during World War II. In other instances, where a species is represented by just the type specimen and no contemporary collections, it has been impossible to decide whether the specimen is part of a variational pattern or sufficiently distinct to maintain as a species. Rather than assign such taxa to other species as synonyms I have decided to treat them as insufficiently known. I have indicated tentative affinities wherever possible.

Arum besserianum Schott in Oesterr. Bot. Zeit. 10: 349 (1858). Type: [NW Ukraine] in Volhinia, *Besser* s.n. (lectotype selected here KW! isolectotype K!).

A. *maculatum* L. subsp. *besserianum* (Schott) Nyman, Consp. Fl. Europ. 755 (1882).

?A. *besserianum* Schott var. *miodoborense* Szafer in Spraw. Komis. Fizjogr. 48: 72 (1914). Type: not designated.

?A. *besserianum* Schott forma *miodoborense* (Szafer) Terpó in Acta Bot. Acad. Sci. Hung. 18: 242 (1973).

A. *orientale* Bieb. subsp. *besserianum* (Schott) Holub in Folia Geobot. Phytotax. 12: 307 (1977) ('besseranum').

Schott stated that the name *A. besserianum* was based on specimens in Besser's herbarium, together with specimens in various other herbaria including Kew. A specimen annotated 'Volhinia' and collected by Besser is present in Kiev, where Besser's main collections are housed, and is thus the best choice for the lectotype.

Schott thought that *A. besserianum* was allied to *A. orientale* but more recently Riedl (1967) cited it as a synonym of *A. alpinum*. The isolectotype at Kew is clearly close to *A. orientale*, especially in both the form of the spadix-appendix and the sterile flowers, and in the spathe being held beneath the leaves.

Some Eastern European botanists accept *A. besserianum* as a 'good' species and Szafer (1914) even described a variety, *A. besserianum* var. *miodoborense*, also referred to as forma *miodoborense* by Terpó (1973), based on differences in the staminode arrangement. Holub (1977) presented a rather rambling paper on the taxonomy and relationships of *A. besserianum*, *A. orientale* and *A. alpinum*, concluding that *A. besserianum* and *A. alpinum* were synonymus and furthermore were not separable from *A. orientale* at any more than subspecific rank. In my opinion there is little to support a close relationship between *A. alpinum* and *A. orientale*. At present it seems best to regard *A. besserianum* as incompletely known.

Further collections from the Ukraine and from neighbouring countries are needed before the status of *A. besserianum* can be properly evaluated.

A. cylindraceum Gasp. in Guss., Fl. Sic. Syn., 2(2): 597 (1844). Type: (Italy) in herbosis montosis; Madonie al piano della battaglia di petralis, *Gasparrini* s.n. (holotype FI!).

A. maculatum L. var. *cylindraceum* (Gasp.) Engler, Pflanzenr. 73 (IV. 23F): 92 (1920) ('*cylindricum*').

The status of this species remains a problem. The type material in Florence is in poor condition. Overall it resembles *A. alpinum* but certain characters, notably the very slender spathe-tube and long spadix-appendix are clearly anomalous. Little can be done to clarify *A. cylindraceum* until further collections are available.

It is interesting to note that if *A. cylindraceum* does prove to be inseparable from *A. alpinum*, then the name *A. cylindraceum* (1844) has priority over *A. alpinum* (1851).

A. guellekense Kotschy *in sched. nom. nud.* and *A. quellekense* Kotschy *in sched. nom. nud.*

It seems that these names apply to the same species. Engler (1879) used the name *A. guellekense*, but in the *Pflanzenreich* account (Engler, 1920) he altered the spelling to *A. quellekense*. Engler stated that he has seen material in Schott's herbarium in Vienna. Although Engler (1879; 1920) referred *A. guellekense* to *A. conophalloides* (i.e. *A. rupicola*), without authentic specimens I feel that it is best to regard *A. guellekense* as an inadequately known taxon.

176

A. kasrunicum Stapf *in sched. nom. nud.*

I have been unable to trace any material of this species. Hruby (1912) and Engler (1920) referred it to *A. conophalloides* which, considering the area of Iran where it was gathered, is not unreasonable.

A. melanopus Boiss., Fl. Orient. 5: 40 (1882). Type: Syria, prope Aleppo, *Haussknecht* s.n. (holotype G–BOIS).

Described from material gathered from Syria. Boissier placed *A. melanopus* in subsection *Ootuberosae*, implying a relationship with *A. maculatum* and *A. italicum*. The type material in Geneva lacks a tuber and, in fact, the tuber was unknown to Boissier.

Notwithstanding the missing tuber, the gross morphology suggests an affinity to *A. orientale* and *A. gratum* rather than *A. maculatum* and *A. italicum*. Unfortunately *A. melanopus* has not been re-collected, although Thiébaut (1953) and Mouterde (1966) treat it as a distinct species. It may be that *A. melanopus* and *A. gratum* represent opposite extremes of a wide spectrum of variation. Until more material is available, especially Lebanese collections, the problem will have to remain unresolved.

A. neumayeri Vis. ex Beck v. Mannag. in Wiss. Mittle. Bos. und der Herceg. 9: 68 (1904). Type: not cited.

Referred to as a synonym of *A. nigrum* by Engler (1920). I have been unable to locate any material with which to confirm this. Other possibilities are *A. orientale* or perhaps even *A. elongatum*.

HYBRIDS

Artificial hybridization in *Arum* has been virtually ignored. Except in one instance (Prime, 1960), where manual pollination of two species was carried out in order to investigate the relationship between the taxa, no pollination experiments have been recorded. This lack of hybridization is in marked contrast to many other genera in the Araceae, i.e. *Zantedeschia* Sprengel, *Anthurium* Schott, *Alocasia* (Schott) G. Don, where numerous artificial hybrids have been produced since the nineteenth century. There are, however, a few natural hybrids in *Arum* which were generally overlooked prior to the 1940s. Today, four hybrids are known and the number of recognized hybrids is likely to increase in the coming years.

The hybrids at present recognized in *Arum* are:

1. **A.** × **sooi** Terpó (*A. alpinum* Schott & Kotschy × *A. maculatum* L.) in Acta Bot. Acad. Sci. Hung. 18: 240 (1973). Type: Western Hungary: Mosonmagyaróvár, Halaszi, *Czimber*, *Erdös* & Terpó 18195 (holotype KEH).
This is the same hybrid as reported by Harmes (1985) who gave the parents as *A. orientale* subsp. *danicum* and *A. maculatum*.

2. **A. apulum** (Carano) Boyce [as *A. apulum* (Carano) Bedalov] × **A. italicum** Miller subsp. **italicum** (reported in Bedalov, 1984).

3. **A. italicum** Miller subsp. **italicum** × **A. maculatum** L. (reported in Beuret, 1977).

4. **A. italicum** Miller subsp. **neglectum** (F. Towns.) Prime × **A. maculatum** L. (reported in Lovis, 1954, Prime, Buckle & Lovis, 1955).

In addition to those above, a number of possible hybrids exists. None of these has been verified as yet. On Cyprus, Smit of the Vrije University, Amsterdam, discovered a colony of *Arum* some years ago that appeared to be a hybrid between *A. hygrophilum* and *A. orientale*. The possibility of a hybrid involving two species from different

179

subsections is interesting and this putative hybrid deserves further study.

As noted under *A. idaeum* and *A. creticum*, there appears to be hybridization between these species on Crete, and in the Middle East populations intermediate between *A. palaestinum* and *A. dioscoridis* indicate a possible hybrid.

BIBLIOGRAPHY

Allioni, C. (1785). Araceae. In *Flora Pedemontana* 2: 228–9. Turin.

Alpinar, K. (1985). Bati Türkiye'de Arum L. (Araceae) türleri ve bu türlerin yumrularinin nişasta ve protein miktarlari. *Doga Tu Bio. D. C.* 9: 473–83. (Chemical analysis).

—— (1986). Bati Türkiye'nin Arum L. (Araceae) türleri üzerinde bazi bulgu ve gözlemler. *Doga Tu Bio. D. C.* 10: 240–53. (Chromosome counts).

Akeroyd, J.R. & Preston, C.D. (1987). Floristic notes from the Aegean region of Greece. *Willdenowia* 16: 354.

ap Rees, T., Wright, B.W. & Fuller, W.A. (1976). Pathways of carbohydrate oxidation during thermogenesis by the spadix of Arum maculatum. *Biochim. Biophys. Acta* 437: 22–35.

——, —— & —— (1977). Measurements of starch breakdown as estimates of glycolysis during thermogenesis by the spadix of Arum maculatum L. *Planta* 134: 53–6.

Arcangeli, G. (1883). Sull'impollinazione in alcune Araceae. *Nuovo Giorn. Bot. Ital.* 15: 72–97.

Ascherson, P.R.A. & Graebner, K.O.R.P.P. (1904). Araceae. In *Synopsis der Mitteleuropäischen Flora* 2,2: 362–90. Leipzig.

Baytop, T. (1982). Deux nouvelles Aracées pour le Turquie. *Journ. Fac. Pharm. Istanbul* 18: 60–4.

Beck, R. von Mannagetta und L., G. (1903). Araceae. In *Flora Bosne, Hercegovine, Novopazarskog Sandzaka* 2: 58–60. Sarajevo.

Bedalov, M. in Löve, A. (1973). IOPB Chromosome Number Reports: XL. *Taxon* 22: 285.

—— (1975a). Cytotaxonomical and phytogeographical investigation of the species Arum italicum Mill. in Jugoslavia. *Acta Bot. Croat.* 34: 143–50.

—— (1975b). Taxonomic problems and distribution of the species Arum nigrum Schott in the Balkan flora. *Problems of the Balkan Flora and Vegetation.* Sofia.

—— (1978). Sur quelques espèces diploïdes du genera Arum L. *Bull. Soc. Neuchâteloise Sci. Nat.* 101: 85–93.

181

—— (1980). Two Arum interesting to the flora of South Italy. *Journées Étude. Systém. et Biogéogr. Médit.* Cagliari C.I.E.S.M. 101–2

—— (1981). Cytotaxonomy of the genus Arum (Araceae) in the Balkans and the Aegean Area. *Bot. Jahrb. Syst.* 102: 183–200.

—— (1982). Die Gattung Arum in den Ostalpenländern. *Stapfia* 10: 95–7.

—— (1984). A new pentaploid of the genus Arum (Araceae). *Bot. Helvetica* 94(2): 385–90.

—— (1985). Scanning electron microscopy of pollen grains of some species of the genus Arum (Araceae). *Pl. Syst. Evol.* 149: 211–16.

—— & Hesse, M. (1989). On some pollen types within Arum (Araceae). *Pl. Syst. Evol.* 166: 41–4.

Beuret, E. (1971). Répatition de quelque Arum des groupes maculatum L. et italicum Miller. *Bull. Soc. Neuchâteloise Sci. Nat.* 94: 29–36.

—— (1972). Contribution d'un Arum diploid en Italie. *Bull. Soc. Neuchâteloise Sci. Nat.* 95: 35–41.

—— (1977). Contribution a l'étude de la distribution géographique et de la physiologie de taxons affines di- et polyploides. *Biblioth. Bot.* 133: 1–80.

Bieberstein, L.B.F.M. von. (1808). Araceae. In *Flora Taurico-Caucasica* 2: 406–7. Charcov.

Blanc, P. (1977a). Contribution à l'étude des Aracées. I. Remarques sur la croissance monopodiale. *Rev. Gén. Bot.* 84: 115–26.

—— (1977b). Contribution à l'étude des Aracées. II. Remarques sur la croissance sympodiale chez l'Anthurium scandens Engler, le Philodendron fenzlii Engler et le Philodendron speciosum Schott. *Rev. Gén. Bot.* 84: 319–31.

Blume, C.L. von (1836) ('1835'). Arum. In *Rumphia* 1: 116–23. Leiden & Amsterdam.

Bogner, J. (1978). A critical list of the Aroid genera. *Aroideana* 1: 63–73.

—— & Nicolson, D.H. (1991). A revised classification of Araceae with dichotomous keys. *Willdenowia* 21: 35–50.

Boissier, P.E. (1853). Araceae. In *Diagnoses Plantarum Orientalium Novarum* 1(13): 5–10. Como.

—— (1882). Araceae. In *Flora Orientalis* 5: 30–45. Geneva & Basle.

Borhidi, A. in Priszter, S. & Borhidi, A. (1967). A mecseki flórajárás (sopiankum) flórájához I. *Bot. Közlem.* 54: 153–4.

Bornmüller, J.F.N. (1914). Zur Flora des Libanon und Antilibanon. *Beih. Bot. Centralbl.* 31: 259–60.

—— (1927). Beiträge zur Flora Mazedoniens III. *Bot. Jahrb. Syst.* 61: 123.

—— & Gauba, E. (1939). Florulae Keredjensis Fundamenta (Plantae Gaubaenae iranicae III). *Feddes Rep. Sp. Nov.* 47: 71.

Bown, D. (1988). *Aroids, plants of the Arum family.* Century, London.

Boyce, P.C. (1986). Observations on Aroids. *Bull. Alpine Gard. Soc.* 54: 35–42.

—— (1987a). A new species of Arum L. from Crete. *Aroideana* 10(1): 6–8.

—— (1987b). A new subspecies of Biarum davisii Turrill from Turkey. *Aroideana* 10(2): 14–15.

—— (1989). A new classification of Arum with keys to the infrageneric taxa. *Kew Bull.* 44: 383–95.

Braun-Blanquet, J. & Maire, R. (1922). Contributions à l'étude de la Flore maroccaine. *Bull. Hist. Nat. l'Afrique Nord.* 3: 20–1.

Braverman, Y. & Koach, J. (1982). Culicoides species found in the inflorescences of Arum elongatum in Israel. *Mosquito News* 42: 516–17.

Briquet, J.I. (1910). Araceae. In *Prodrome de la Flore Corse* 1: 235–9. Geneva, Basle & Lyon.

Buc'hoz, P.J. (1775). *Histoire Universelle du règne végétal*, 8, t.2. Paris.

Carano, E. (1934). Un nuovo elemento della flora meridionale d'Italia: l'Arum nigrum Schott var. apulum. *Ann. Bot.* 20: 579–85, t.17.

Cavara, F. & Grande, L. (1911). Esplorazioni Botaniche in Basilicata. *Bull. Orto Bot. Regia Univ. Napoli* 3: 409–10.

Chen, J. & Meeuse, B.J.D. (1971). Production of free indole by some aroids. *Acta Bot. Neerl.* 20: 627–37.

Chodat, L. (1923). Géo-Botanique de Majorque. *Bull. Soc. Bot. Genève* 15: 193–5.

Clusius, C. (1601). *Rariorum Plantarum Historia* 4: 73, t.49. Antwerp.

Contandriopoulos, J. (1962). Recherches sur la flore endemique de la Corse et sur les origines. *Ann. Faculté Sci. Marseille* 32: 1–354.

Corbière, L. (1898). Araceae. In *Nouvelle flore de Normandie, 2nd. suppl.* Caen.

Cousturier, P. & Gandoger, M. (1917). Herborisations en Crète (1913–1914). *Bull. Soc. Bot. France* 63: 1–15.

Czetz, A. (1872). *Erdély. Múz.-Egyl. Evk.* 6: 11.

Dalmer, M. (1880). Ueber die Leitung der Pollenschläuche bei den Angiospermen. *Jenaische Z. Naturwiss.* 14: 530–66.

Dihoru, G. (1970a). Taxonomische Aspekte einiger Arum-arten. *Bot. Közlem.* 57: 201–6.

—— (1970b). Morpho-taxonomische Aspekte einiger Arum-arten. *Rev. Roum. Biol. Ser. Bot.* 15: 71–84.

Dormer, K.J. (1960). The truth about pollination in Arum L. *New Phytol.* 59: 298–301.

Drummond, D.C. & Hammond, P.M. (1991). Insects visiting Arum dioscoridis Sm. & A. orientale M. Bieb. In *Entomologist's Mon. Mag.* 127: 151–6.

Dufour, J.-M.L. in Lapeyrouse, P.P. de (1818). *Histoire Abrégée des Plantes Pyrénées. Supplement*, 143. Toulouse.

Dulac, J. (1867). Araceae. In *Flore de Départment des Hautes Pyrénées*, 46–7. Paris.

Durand, E.A. & Barratte, G. (1910). Araceae. In *Florae Libycae Prodromus*, 242–3. Geneva.

El Gadi, A. (1977). Araceae. In *Flora of Libya* 41: 1–9. Tripoli.

Ender, E.E. (1864). Arum & Gymnomesium. In *Index Aroidearum*, 22–8, 46. Berlin.

Endlicher, S.F.L. (1837). Arum. In *Genera Plantarum* 3: 235. Vienna.

Engler, A. (1877). Vergleichende Untersuchungen über die morphologischen Verhältnisse der Araceae II. *Nova Acta Leop.* 39: 158–231.

—— (1879) Arum. In A. & C. De Candolle (eds), *Monographiae Phanerogamarum* 2: 580–97. Paris.

—— (1889) Arum. In Engler, A. & Prantl, K.A.E., *Die Natürlichen Pflanzenfamilien*. Leipzig.

—— (1905). Pothoideae. In Engler, A. (ed.), *Das Pflanzenreich* 21 (IV. 23F): 1–330. Berlin.

—— (1911). Lasioideae. In Engler, A. (ed.), *Das Pflanzenreich* 48 (IV. 23C): 1–130. Berlin.

—— (1915). Philodendroideae. In Engler, A. (ed.), *Das Pflanzenreich* 64 (IV. 23Dc): 1–78. Berlin.

—— (1920). Aroideae. In Engler, A. (ed.), *Das Pflanzenreich* 73 (IV. 23F): 1–249. Berlin.

—— & Krause, K. (1908). Monsteroideae. In Engler, A. (ed.), *Das Pflanzenreich* 37 (IV. 23B): 1–139. Berlin.

—— & —— (1912). Philodendroideae. In Engler, A. (ed.), *Das Pflanzenreich* 55 (IV. 23Da): 1–134. Berlin.

—— & —— (1920). Colocasioideae. In Engler, A. (ed.), *Das Pflanzenreich* 71 (IV. 23E): 2–139. Berlin.

Fernandez, O. (1952). In *Chem. Abstr.* 46: 2321.

Forziano, M.J., Crisci, J.V. & Delucchi, G. (1991). Arum italicum (Araceae) especie naturalizada de la flora Argentina. *Kurtziana* 21: 237–41.

French, J.C. (1985a). Patterns of endothecial wall thickenings in Araceae: Subfamilies Pothoideae and Monsteroideae. *Amer. J. Bot.* 72: 472–86.

—— (1985b). Patterns of endothecial wall thickening in Araceae: Subfamilies Calloideae, Lasioideae and Philodendroideae. *Bot. Gaz. (Crawfordsville)* 146: 521–33.

—— (1986a). Patterns of endothecial wall thickenings in Araceae: Subfamilies Colocasioideae, Aroideae and Pistioideae. *Bot. Gaz. (Crawfordsville)* 147: 166–79.

—— (1986b). Patterns of stamen vasculature in the Araceae. *Amer. J. Bot.* 73: 434–49.

—— (1986c). Ovular vasculature in Araceae. *Bot. Gaz. (Crawfordsville)* 148: 478–95.

—— (1987a). Systematic occurrence of sclerotic hypodermis in roots of Araceae. *Amer. J. Bot.* 74: 891–903.

—— (1987b). Structure of ovular and placental trichomes of Araceae. *Bot. Gaz. (Crawfordsville)* 148: 198–208.

—— (1987c). Systematic survey of resin canals in roots of Araceae. *Bot. Gaz. (Crawfordsville)* 148: 360–71.

—— (1988). Systematic occurrence of anastomosing lacticifers in Araceae. *Bot. Gaz. (Crawfordsville)* 149: 71–81.

—— & Tomlinson, P.B. (1981a). Vascular patterns in stems of Araceae: Subfamily Pothoideae. *Amer. J. Bot.* 68: 713–29.

—— & —— (1981b). Vascular patterns in stems of Araceae: Subfamily Monsteroideae. *Amer. J. Bot.* 68: 1115–29.

—— & —— (1981c). Vascular patterns in stems of Araceae: Subfamilies Calloideae and Lasioideae. *Bot. Gaz. (Crawfordsville)* 142: 366–81.

—— & —— (1981d). Vascular patterns in stems of Araceae: Subfamily Philodendroidcae. *Bot. Gaz. (Crawfordsville)* 142: 550–63.

—— & —— (1983). Vascular patterns in stems of Araceae: Subfamilies Colocasioideae, Aroideae and Pistioideae. *Amer. J. Bot.* 70: 756–71.

Frohne, D. & Pfänder, H.J. (1984). *A Colour Altas of Poisonous Plants.* Wolfe, London.

Fuchs, L. (1542). *De Historia Stirpium Commentarii.* Basle.

Gasparrini, G. in Gussone, G. (1844). *Florae Siculae Synopsis* 2, 2: 597. Naples.

Ghahreman, A. (1983). Arum giganteum (Araceae), a new species from W Iran. *Iran. J. Bot.* 2: 79–81.

Gori, I. (1958). Il numero die chromosomi dell'Arum nigrum Schott var. apulum Carano. *Caryologia* 10: 454–6.

Grigson, G. (1955). *The Englishman's Flora.* Phoenix House, London.

Grayum, M.H. (1984). 'Palynology and phylogeny of the Araceae'. Ph.D. Thesis, Univ. Massachusetts, Amherst. (Unpublished).

Green, M.L. (1929). In Sprague, T.A., *et al.* (eds.), *Nomenclature proposals by British botanists*, 1–203. HMSO, London.

Greuter, W. (1984). Les Arum de la Crète. *Bot. Helvetica* 94: 15–22.

—— *et al.* (1988). *International Code of Botanical Nomenclature.* Koeltz Scientific Books, Germany.

Grey-Wilson, C. & Mathew, B. (1981). *Bulbs, the bulbous plants of Europe and their allies.* Collins, London.

Harmes, P. (1982). Leaf polymorphism in Arum maculatum L. *Watsonia* 14: 70.

—— (1985). Arum orientale subsp. danicum × maculatum, an overlooked intespecific hybrid. *Bot. Soc. Brit. Isles, News* 39: 26.

—— (1986). Seed morphology in Arum maculatum L. *Watsonia* 16: 176–7.

Haussknecht, H.C. (1890). Floristische Notizen. *Mitt. Geogr. Ges. (Thüringen) Jena* 9: 22.

Heim, H., Chaulinguet, J. & Hebert, A. (1897). Sur les principes actifs de quelques Aroidés. *Compt. Rend. Hebd. Séances Acad. Sci.* 134: 1368–70.

Hoffmansegg, J.C. von (1826). *Verzeichniss Pflanzenkulturen* 2: 25. Dresden.

Holub, J. (1977). New Names in Phenerogamae 5. *Folia Geobot. Phytotax.* 12: 293–311.

Horvat, I. (1949). Ujabb adatok Baranya flórájának ismeretéhez. Additamenta nova ad cognitionem florae comitati Baranya. *Borbàsia* 9: 129–30.

Hoschedé, J.P. (1903). *Bull. Acad. Géogr. Bot.* 12: 204.

Hruby, J. (1912). Le Genre Arum. *Bull. Soc. Bot. Genève* 4: 113–60, 330–71.

Huxley, A. & Taylor, W. (1977). Araceae. In *Flowers of Greece and the Aegean.* 157–8, figs. 418, 419 & 420. Chatto & Windus, London.

Irmisch, T. (1874). Beiträge zur vergleichenden Morphologie der Pflanzen. 5. Abteilung. Ueber einige Aroideen. *Abh. Naturf. Ges. Görlitz* 13: 1–48.

James, W.O. & Beevers, H. (1950). The respiration of Arum spadix. *New Phytol.* 49: 353

Janchen, M.E. (1960). Araceae. In *Catalogus Florae Austriae* 1: 876–7. Vienna.

Jones, G.E. (1957). 'Chromosome numbers and phylogenetic relationships in the Araceae'. Ph.D. Thesis, Univ. Virginia, Charlotteville. (Unpublished).

Knoll, F. (1926). Die Arum-Blütenstände und ihre besucher. *Abh. K. K. Zool.-Bot. Ges. Wien.* 12: 383–481.

Koach, J. (1986) Araceae. In Feinbrun, D.N. (ed.), *Flora Palaestina* 4: 330–40. Jerusalem.

—— (1987). 'Bio-ecological studies of flowering and pollination in Israeli Araceae.' Ph.D. Thesis, Univ. Tel-Aviv. (Unpublished).

Kononov, V. & Moljkova, I. (1974). Rod aronnik (Arum L.) v SSR. *Novosti Sist. Vyssh. Rast.* 11: 75–83. (Arum in the USSR: chromosome counts and investigation of putative natural hybrids).

Krause, K. (1908). Calloideae in Engler, A. (ed.), *Das Pflanzenreich* 37 (IV. 23B): 140–61. Berlin.

Kullenberg, B. (1953). Observationer över Arum-pollinerare i Libanons kustomåde. *Svensk Bot. Tidskr.* 47: 24–9.

Lack, A.J. & Diaz, A. (1991). The pollination of Arum maculatum L. – a historical review and new observations. *Watsonia* 18: 333–42.

Lamarck, J.B.A.P.M. de (1778). Araceae. In *Flore Française* 3: 537–9. Paris.

Lamb, A. (1956). An investigation of the efficiency of the pollination mechanism in Lords-and-Ladies. *Blundell's School Scientific Society's Magazine* 2: 33–7.

Lecat, P. (1942). Note sur la répartition de l'acide ascorbique chez trois plantes du genre Arum. *Bull. Soc. Bot. France* 89: 234–6.

Ledebour, C.F. von (1853). Araceae. In *Flora Rossica* 4: 8–13. Stuttgart.

Li, H. (1979). Arum. In Wu, C.Y. & Li, H. (eds), *Flora Republicae Popularis Sinicae* 13(2): 100–1. Kunming.

Linnaeus, C. (1753). *Species Plantarum* 2: 964–8. Stockholm.

Linnaeus fil., C. (1782). *Supplementum Plantarum*, 410. Braunschweig.

Lobelius, M. (1576). *Plantarum seu Stirpium Historia*. Antwerp.

Loiseleur-Deslongchamps, J.L.A. (1807). Araceae. In *Flora Gallica* 2: 616–17. Paris.

Löve, A. & Kjellqvist, E. (1973). Cytotaxonomy of Spanish plants II. Monocotyledons. *Lagascalia* 3: 147–82.

Lovis, J.D. (1954). A wild Arum hybrid. *Bot. Soc. Brit. Isles, Proc.* 1: 97.

Maire, R. & Weiller, A. (1957). Araceae. In *Flore de l'Afrique du Nord* 4: 232–49. Lechevalier, Paris.

Marchant, C.J. (1972). Chromosome variation in Araceae: IV. Areae. *Kew Bull.* 26: 395–404.

—— (1973). Chromosome variation in Araceae: V. Acoreae to Lasieae. *Kew Bull.* 28: 199–210.

Marchi, P., Capinieri, R. & D'Amato, G. (1974). Numeri cromosomici per la flora Italiana: 182–9. *Inf. Bot. Ital.* 6: 303–18.

Mayo, S.J. (1980). Aroid symposium at Selby gardens. *Aroideana* 3: 69–71.

—— (1986). 'Systematics of Philodendron Schott (Araceae) with special reference to inflorescence characters'. Ph.D. Thesis, Univ. Reading (Unpublished).

—— & Meikle, R.D. (1985). Araceae. In Meikle, R.D. (ed.), *Flora of Cyprus* 2: 1664–71. RBG, Kew.

Meeuse, B.J.D. (1975). Thermogenic respiration in aroids. *Annual Rev. Pl. Physiol.* 26: 117–26.

—— (1985). Physiological and biochemical aspects of thermogenic respiration in the aroid appendix. In Palmer, J.M. (ed.), *The physiology and biochemistry of plant respiration* 47–58. Society for Experimental Biology. Seminar series 20.

—— & Raskin, I. (1988). Sexual reproduction in the arum lily family, with emphasis on thermogenicity. *Sex. Plant. Reprod.* 1: 3–15.

Mill, R.R. (1983). Araceae. In Davis, P.H. (ed.), Materials for a Flora of Turkey XXXVIII: Araceae, Dioscoreaceae, Liliaceae. *Notes Roy. Bot. Gard. Edinb.* 41: 45–7.

—— (1984). Araceae. In Davis, P.H. (ed.), *Flora of Turkey* 8: 41–63. Edinburgh University Press.

—— & Alpinar, K. (1988). *Araceae.* In Davis, P.H. *et al.* (eds), *Flora of Turkey* 10: 218–21, 236.

Miller, P. (1768). Arum. In *Gardeners Dictionary* (edn.8) no.2. London.

Mouterde, P. (1966). Araceae. In *Nouvelle Flore du Liban et de la Syrie.* 1: 182–94. Beirut.

Mutel, A. (1836). Araceae. In *Flore de la France* 3: 339–41. Paris.

Nashe, T. (1589) in preface to Greene, R., *Menaphon* (reprinted 1927).

Nehmeh, M. (1978). *Wild Flowers of Lebanon*, 135–6, pl. 13–15. Beirut.

Nielsen, H. & Ugelvig, J. (1986). Dansk Arum. *Urt* 3: 81–5.

Nyman, C.F. (1882). Araceae. In *Conspectus Flora Europaeae*, 753–7. Volhinia.

Pampanini, R. (1928). Arum italicum Miller var. typicum Engler forma purpurascens Pamp. f. n. In *Nuovo Giorn. Bot. Ital.* 35: 302.

Paoli, P. & Romagnoli, G. (1976). La Flora vascolare dell'isola di Montecristo (Arcipelago toscano). *Webbia* 30: 303–456.

Petersen, G. (1989). Cytology and Systematics of Araceae. *Nord. J. Bot.* 9: 119–66.

Petter, F. (1852). *Botanischer Wegweiser in der Gegend von Spalato* no. 114. Zara.

Pfeiffer, L.G.K. (1873). Arum. In *Nomenclator Botanicus* 1(1): 283–4. Kassel.

—— (1874). Gymnomesium. In *Nomenclator Botanicus* 1(2): 1525. Kassel.

Phillips, R. (1977). *Wild Flowers of Britain.* Pan, London.

—— & Rix, E.M. (1989). *Bulbs.* Pan, London.

Pignatti, S. (1982). Araceae. In *Flora d'Italia* 3: 624–9. Bologna.

Polunin, O. (1980). Araceae. In *Flowers of Greece and the Balkans*, 508–9, pl. 61, fig. 1818. Oxford University Press.

Prime, C.T. (1960). *Lords and Ladies.* Collins, London.

—— (1961). Taxonomy and nomenclature in some species of the genus Arum L. *Watsonia* 5: 106–9.

—— (1978). Short Notes. *J. Linn. Soc., Bot.* 76: 384.

—— (1980). Araceae. In Tutin, T.G., *et al.* (eds), *Flora Europaea* 5: 268–72. Cambridge University Press.

——, Buckle, O. & Lovis, J.D. (1955). The distribution and ecology of Arum neglectum in southern England. *Proc. Bot. Soc. Brit. Isles* 1: 287–96.

——, —— & —— (1960). The distribution and ecology of Arum neglectum in southern England and Wales. *Proc. Bot. Soc. Brit. Isles* 4: 26–32.

Raskin, J. *et al.* (1987). Salycylic acid is a natural inducer of heat production in plants. Item no. 691. *Plant Physiology (Supplement)* 83: 115.

Ray, T.S. (1987a). Leaf types in the Araceae. *Amer. J. Bot.* 74: 1359–72.

—— (1987b). Diversity of shoot organization in the Araceae. *Amer. J. Bot.* 74: 1373–87.

Rechinger, K.H. (1943). Araceae. In *Flora Aegaea*, 843–6. Vienna.

Regel, E. von (1873). Descriptiones plantarum novarum in regionibus Turkestanicus A cl. viris Fedjenko, Korolkow, Kuschakewz et Krause collectis. *Acta Hort. Petrop.* 2: 407.

—— (1879). Descriptiones plantarum novarum et minus cognitarum VII. *Acta Hort. Petrop.* 6: 489.

Reichenbach, H.G.L. (1830). Araceae. In *Flora Germania Excursoria*, 138. Leipzig.

—— (1845). Araceae. In *Icones Florae Germanicae*, 4–7, t.6–13. Leipzig.

Richter, J. (1890). Arum. In *Plantae Europeae* 1: 172–3. Leipzig.

Ridley, H.N. (1938). Arum neglectum (Towns.) Ridl. *J. Bot.* 76: 144–7.

Riedl, H. (1963). Araceae. In Rechinger, K.H. (ed.) *Flora Iranica*, 1–10. Graz.

—— (1967). Die infraspezifischen einheiten von Arum maculatum in Mitteleuropa. *Phyton* 12: 159–68.

—— (1980). Araceae. In Hegi, G. (ed.), *Illustrierte Flora von Mitteleuropa* 2(1,5): 321–4. Berlin, Hamburg.

—— (1981). A new species of Arum from Iraq. *Kew Bull.* 36: 643–4.

—— (1985). Araceae. In Townsend, C.C. *et al* (eds), *Flora of Iraq* 8: 185–203. Baghdad.

Ross-Craig, S. (1973). *Drawings of British Plants* 30: pl. 39–40b. Bell & Hyman, London.

Rouy, G. (1912). Araceae. In *Flora de France* 13: 273–82. Paris.

Schmucker, T. (1925). Beiträge zur Biologie und Physiologie von Arum maculatum. *Flora* 18: 460.

Schott, H.W. (1832). Araceae. In Schott, H.W. & Endlicher, S.F.L., *Melatamata Botanica*: 16–22. Vienna.

—— (1855). Pflanzenskizzen. *Oesterr. Bot. Wochenbl.* 5: 17–20.

—— (1856). Gymnomesium & Arum. In *Synopsis Aroidearum*, 8–15. Vienna.

—— (1857a). Über Arum dioscoridis. *Oesterr. Bot. Wochenbl.* 7: 173–5.

—— (1857b). Pflanzen-skizzen. *Oesterr. Bot. Wochenbl.* 7: 213–14.

—— (1858a). Aroideen-skizzen. *Oesterr. Bot. Zeit.* 8: 349–51.

—— (1858b). *Genera Aroidearum*, t.12, 13. Vienna.

—— (1859). *Icones Aroidearum*, t.39, 40. Vienna.

—— (1860). Gymnomesium & Arum. In *Prodromus Systematis Aroidearum*, 73–102. Vienna.

—— (1861). Aroideologisches. *Bonplandia* 9: 367–9.

—— (1862). Aroideologisches. *Bonplandia* 10: 147–8.

—— & Kotschy, T. (1851). Ein neues Arum. *Bot. Zeitung (Berlin)* 9: 285.

Sibthorp, J. & Lindley, J. (1840). Arum. In *Flora Graeca* 10: t.947. London.

Smith, J.E. (1813) in Sibthorp, J. & Smith, J.E., *Flora Graecae Prodromus*, 245. London.

Smith, B.N. & Meeuse, B.J.D. (1966). Production of volatile amines and skatoles at anthesis of some arum lily species. *Pl. Physiol. (Lancaster)* 41: 343–57.

Stapf, O. (1885). Die Botanischen Ergebnisse Polak'shen Expedition nach Persien. *Denkschr. Kaiserl. Akad. Wiss., Math.-Naturwiss. Kl.* 50: 6.

Steven, C. von (1857). Verzeichniss der auf der taurischen Halbinsel wildwachsenden Pflanzen. *Bull. Soc. Imp. Naturalistes Moscou* 30: 66–7.

Szafer, W. (1914). Beitrag zur Kenntnis der Flora von Miodobory. *Spraw. Komis. Fizjogr.* 48: 72.

Tabernaemontanus, J.T. (1590). *Eicones Plantarum*. Frankfurt.

Takhtadjan, A.L. (1982). Araceae. In *Zhizn' Rastenii (Tsvetkovyee Rasteniya)* 6: 466–92, t.64(2). Moscow.

Targione-Tozzetti, O. (1813). *Instituzioni Botaniche* (edn. 2) 278–9. Florence.

Tchihatcheff, P. de (1860). Araceae. In *Asie Mineure (Bot.)* 2: 643–8. Paris.

Terpó, A. (1971). Arum-rendszertani kutatások Magyarországon. *Bot. Közlem* 58: 153–63.

—— (1973). Kritische revision der Arum-Arten des Karpatenbeckens. *Acta Bot. Acad. Sci. Hung.* 18: 215–55.

Tourneforte, J.P. (1719). *Institutions Rei Herbariae.* Paris.

Townsend, F. (1883). Araceae. In *Flora of Hampshire*, 326–7. London.

Thiébaut, J. (1953). Araceae. In *Flore Libano-Syrienne* 3: 230–34.

Unverricht, C. (1854). *Verh. Mitth. Siebenbürg. Vereins Naturwiss. Hermannstadt.* 5: 173.

Vellozo, J.M. da C. (1827). Araceae. In *Flora Fluminensis* 9: t.107. Rio de Janeiro.

Visiani, R. de (1904) in Beck, R. von Mannagetta und L., G. Flora von Bosnien de Herzegowina und des Sanzaks Novipazar. *Wiss. Mitt. Bos. Herceg.* 9: 407–518.

Webb, P.B. & Berthelot, S. (1848). Araceae. In *Histoire Naturel des Iles Canaries.* 3,2: 293–6. Paris.

Willdenow, C.L. von (1805). *Species Plantarum* (edn.4), 486. Berlin.

Zakharyeva, O.I. & Astanova, S.B. (1968). Chromosome numbers of some wild species of flowering plants of Middle Asia. *Rep. Acad. Sci. Tadzhik SSR.* 2: 72–5.

—— & Makushenka, L.M. (1969). Chromosome numbers of Monocotyledons belonging to the families Liliaceae, Iridaceae, Amaryllidaceae and Araceae. *Bot. Zhurn.* 54(8): 1213–27.

Zelentzky, N.M. (1906). Araceae. In *Prodromus Flora Tauricae*, 324. Odessa.

INDEX TO PLANT NAMES

Accepted names are given in bold type; synonyms are in *italic* type.

193

195